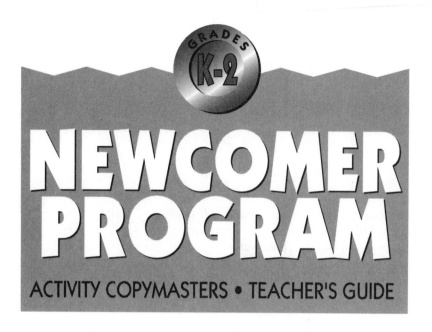

GRADES K-2
NEWCOMER PROGRAM
ACTIVITY COPYMASTERS • TEACHER'S GUIDE

JUDIE HAYNES

PRENTICE HALL REGENTS

Publisher: *Marilyn Lindgren*
Development Editor: *Susan Cosentino*
Electronic Production Editors: *Steven D. Greydanus/Nicole Cypher*
Manufacturing Manager: *Dave Dickey*
Electronic Image Production Supervisor: *Todd Ware*
Electronic Image Production/Scanning: *Marita Froimson*
Art Director: *Wanda España*
Interior Design: *Wanda España/Steven D. Greydanus*
Cover Design: *Wanda España*

PRENTICE HALL REGENTS

Printed in the United States of America

10   9   8   7   6   5   4

ISBN   0-13-369257-4

This book is dedicated to

my husband, Joe,

whose love and caring

over the past thirty years

have greatly enriched my life.

═══════════ ACKNOWLEDGMENTS ═══════════

Very special thanks to Elizabeth Claire, my co-author in writing *The Classroom Teacher's ESL Survival Kits #1* and *#2*. Working with Betty was comparable to getting a graduate degree in writing. Thanks, Betty, for all your great ideas, for teaching me so much, for encouraging me to do this solo project, and especially for being a great friend and mentor. I treasure your untold hours of advice and guidance.

I'd like to thank all the River Edge classroom teachers who have shown such commitment to their ESL students. These dedicated professionals have provided a caring atmosphere for ESL students and have given me valuable feedback on materials. I have learned a tremendous amount from all of them. Thanks also to the River Edge administrators and Board of Education.

I'd also like to acknowledge some of the very special parents who volunteer their time and are committed to the ESL students at River Edge Schools. Our second-language learners have greatly benefited from their gift of time. First, thanks to those bilingual parents who helped me start a volunteer program: Izume Iwase, Ki Hwang, Myung-joo Yun, Akiko Kono, and Yasuko Kamimura. A special recognition must be given to Kazuko Taketomi, whose dedication to helping ESL students was truly exceptional. I'd also like to thank some of the parents who have been outstanding volunteers over the past few years: Chung-youn Min, Yoshi Miyasaka, Mi-yung Lee, Jin-kyung Lee, Takako Tamaki, Dong-wha Lee, Kazuko Nakamura, Sumi Ito, Mi-jung Kim, Nancy Chiang, Michiko Levine, Kazuya Curran, and Hiroko Tomita and Hee-ok Cho.

Thanks to my supportive family: my children Joe, Charles, and Jennifer; my son-in-law, Brian; and my mother, Doris Horne.

Thanks to Dr. Liliane Gaffney of Fairleigh Dickinson University in Teaneck, New Jersey. Everything important I learned about teaching, I learned from Dr. Gaffney, whose example was truly inspirational.

Thanks to my good friend, Judy O'Loughlin, for listening, caring, and sharing.

CONTENTS

▲▼▲

TEACHER'S GUIDE

TEACHING NEWCOMERS

This book has been written to help you, your new students, and all future non-English-speaking students who find their way into your class. The materials are designed to help you establish a nurturing environment for the new second-language learners in your classroom and to maximize the learning opportunities for them. Newcomers vary a great deal in language and literacy skills. This program provides activities and teacher suggestions that address the varied backgrounds and needs of your newcomer students. As you work with new second-language learners, try to create multiple avenues through which they can acquire language. Get help wherever you can: buddies, cross-grade tutors, parent volunteers, administrators, ESL and bilingual teachers. Take advantage of the invaluable resources within the school community.

USING THE NEWCOMER PROGRAM

The **K-2 Newcomer Program** is divided into two sections. The first part is the Teacher's Guide. It includes teaching tips and strategies for working with newcomers as well as multilevel instructions for the Newcomer Activity Pages, which make up the second part of this book.

Teacher's Guide The first part of the Teacher's Guide contains useful information for teachers of beginning-level limited-English-proficient students. Your time is limited and it is tempting to go directly to the activity pages. Nevertheless, you will save yourself confusion and frustration if you read the first twelve pages of this book. This section offers suggestions for welcoming and working with your newcomers. In addition, it details exactly how to set up (or help classroom teachers set up) ESL Learning Centers, how to make an individualized Starter Pack (a packet of materials for newly arrived students), and how to use bilingual parent volunteers to help meet your newcomers' academic, social, and emotional needs. The Teacher's Guide also includes instructions for using the activity pages. You will find objectives for each activity type as well as multilevel directions and extension activities designed to help you tailor the materials to the needs of your students.

Newcomer Activity Pages This part contains 173 beginning-level activity pages developed for ESL students in kindergarten through second grade. The activity pages, intended for newcomers who may have to work independently while the teacher is busy with the rest of the class, can be used in the ESL, bilingual, or mainstream classroom. Although much of the work is individual in nature, the activity pages can be utilized to encourage interaction with other students in the class.

These reproducible activities will help children to acquire the basic vocabulary needed to ease into ESL or regular classes. The pages are three-hole-punched and perforated for your convenience. You may wish to have your newcomers create an ESL folder to organize and keep their activity pages.

WORKING WITH NEWCOMERS

Working with newcomers is both exciting and challenging. In this section you will find a variety of suggestions that will help you ease the newcomer's transition to his or her new academic setting and create numerous and varied learning opportunities. Do not expect to do everything that is mentioned here at once. Remember to get help wherever you can by using the rich resources around you: buddies, cross-grade tutors, parent volunteers, administrators, ESL and bilingual teachers.

UNDERSTANDING THE STAGES OF LANGUAGE ACQUISITION

All new learners of English progress through the same stages to acquire language, regardless of their home language. However, the length of time a particular student spends at each stage of learning may vary quite a bit. The four predictable stages of language acquisition are Preproduction, Early Production, Speech Emergence, and Nearly-Fluent.

1 Preproduction

At first, students need to spend a lot of time listening. At this initial preproduction stage, language learners usually do not produce their own language but rather respond in nonverbal ways. Provide activities geared to tap students' knowledge, but do not force production. Pointing, labeling, and drawing activities work well. Some students may repeat everything you say. Keep in mind that they are not producing their own language but are simply parroting you. Listening is difficult for newcomers at this stage, and activities should provide some clues to meaning. The use of props, visuals, and manipulatives will help increase your students' levels of comprehension. Be sure to make language comprehensible to new learners of English from the very first day.

2 Early Production

The next stage is early production. Students now have a small, active vocabulary and feel ready to speak. Try to ask yes/no and either/or questions that enable your students to respond with one- or two-word answers and show their understanding. Asking simple *who, what,* and *where* questions also allows students to demonstrate their comprehension of material and their ability to communicate.

3 Speech Emergence

The third stage is speech emergence. There is a noticeable increase in listening comprehension as well as in speech production. Students will try to speak using phrases and short sentences and will begin to manipulate the social language of the classroom. Encourage students to express themselves and communicate with language. Ask *how* and *why* questions that elicit short-sentence answers. At this stage, language learners will be able to begin participating in many of the mainstream academic subjects.

4 Nearly-Fluent

The last stage is nearly-fluent. Students understand what is said in the classroom. They can express their ideas comprehensibly with minimal errors in both oral and written communication and are able to read most grade-level material. Ask open-ended questions that allow students to create with language and to speak in complex sentences and paragraphs. Second-language learners in the primary grades will probably no longer need extra help when they reach this stage.

It is important to be aware of the language stages of your students so that you don't set unrealistic expectations for them. All of your newcomers need an opportunity to show that they can do work in English. A student may not be speaking yet, but that doesn't mean that he or she cannot function in your classroom. It is your job to provide materials and create situations that will help your students gain confidence in their language abilities. The more comfortable they are in your classroom and the greater their self-esteem, the readier they will be to learn.

CREATING A LANGUAGE-NURTURING ENVIRONMENT

The newcomer's first days in the American school setting can produce much anxiety and stress in the young learner. It is critical, therefore, to create as warm and welcoming an atmosphere as possible. Lowering the "affective filter" not only contributes to the language development of the child but also allows for a more rapid integration of the child into the academic setting. Below are suggestions for welcoming the newcomer and creating a language-nurturing environment.

Sensitize mainstream students to the newcomers' challenges. Whether you are an ESL, bilingual, or mainstream teacher, you realize the need to prepare English-speaking peers for the arrival of a newcomer. You want them to accept and help the new learners of English in the lunchroom, on the playground, on the bus, in their neighborhoods, as well as in the classroom. The first step is to help mainstream students become sensitive to the challenges the newcomers face. If you are a mainstream teacher, ask your students to imagine that their parents take them to another country to live. Brainstorm with them how they would feel. How would they want the students in their new school to treat them? How would they communicate with their classmates? How would they go about making friends? If you are an ESL or bilingual teacher, you may have additional ideas to share with mainstream teachers for preparing mainstream students for the arrival of a newcomer.

Be aware of the effects of culture shock. The newcomers in your class are suffering from some degree of culture shock. They have been separated from family members, friends, their school, and home language and culture. Being in a strange place and losing the power to communicate can create a feeling of helplessness and loneliness. Since newcomers' parents often do not know what to expect either, they are unable to guide and reassure their children. Don't underestimate the results of culture shock. Children can be devastated by the emotional upheaval caused by moving to a new culture. They may develop physical ailments such as stomachaches, hair loss, headaches, bowel upsets, and incontinence. They may also display a wide variety of unusual behavior such as tantrums, crying, aggression, depression, a tendency to withdraw, and sleeplessness.

Often, newcomers are confused by the seemingly unstructured discipline of American schools and may react with undisciplined behavior. Have a bilingual parent volunteer or older student explain what the rules are. Setting definite guidelines and expectations for your classroom is an important step in mitigating discipline problems.

Create a nurturing environment. You can alleviate many of the newcomers' fears by creating an atmosphere of acceptance and welcome in your class. The first weeks are crucial. A good relationship with you and other students in the class will provide newcomers with a great deal of the support needed to cope with challenges. This can't be emphasized enough. The more comfortable newcomers feel in your classroom, the more quickly they will learn. The more anxiety students experience, the less language they will comprehend. Focus on the positive. Give lots of encouragement and praise for what the students *can* do, and create frequent opportunities for their success in your class. Be careful not to call on them to perform alone above their level of competence.

●●●●●●●●

Pronounce the newcomer's name correctly. Your new students have lost so much, don't also let them lose their name. Write a newcomer's name on the board correctly with a phonetic translation. Ask parents, bilingual volunteers, or same-language peers which part of the name is the family name and which is the given name. Practice until you can say it correctly. Don't Americanize a student's name unless the parents have requested it.

●●●●●●●●

Make ID cards for newcomers. Write the newcomer's name, home address, telephone number, and school address on an index card and give it to parents when they register their child. The card should be carried or worn by the child every day. Make sure that each new student is personally accompanied to a parent or guardian or put on the correct bus at the end of the school day. More than one newly arrived student has become lost during the first few days at school, and this is a terrifying experience for everyone.

●●●●●●●●

Label things in your room. Expose your newcomers to beginning English vocabulary by labeling classroom objects. Photocopy a complete set of labels (pages 3–8) for each of the different languages spoken in your classroom. Ask a native speaker of each language to translate the words and write the translations below the English. Depending on the number of languages spoken in your classroom, you may have one or more labels on each classroom object. Although newcomers may not be literate in their own language, they will recognize the written form of their language and feel proud that it is displayed in your room.

●●●●●●●●

Send newcomers on a tour of the school. If possible, have same-language older students take your newcomers on a tour of the important places in your school. (Some schools make a video tour for newcomers and their parents.) Reduce your students' anxiety by teaching them the route to the lunchroom and to the bus or to the parent pick-up spot. If appropriate for your students at this point, use the activity on pages 81 and 82, *Places in your School.*

✔ Have a bilingual student or parent show newcomers where the bathrooms are and explain what the rules are for leaving the room. An embarrassing accident can have a lasting effect on the child's adjustment.

Schools in many countries do not conduct fire drills. Before newcomers start school, have a bilingual person explain what a fire drill is. The noise from the alarm can be very frightening to a new arrival.

●●●●●●●●

Assign buddies. A buddy who speaks the newcomer's language is a wonderful asset, particularly immediately following the newcomer's arrival. During the adjustment phase, the peer buddy can help ease the newcomer into his or her new environment. Peer interaction of this sort is a great self-esteem builder for the bilingual buddy and provides the newcomer with a friend. You may want to rotate buddies so that students do not become too dependent on one person and the bilingual buddy does not miss too much work.

Use English-speaking buddies, too. You will need to help these buddies learn how to work with non-English speakers. Reward those students who take their job seriously. Keep in mind that peer buddies have a more limited use when students are between 5 and 8 years old. Remember that young bilingual students are not always reliable translators of information. Following are some things your peer buddies can do with your newcomers.

- Help them learn the classroom routine.
- Take them to the office, nurse, or ESL class and back again.
- Sit with them in the lunchroom.
- Learn how to communicate with them using gestures and short phrases.
- Teach them the ABCs, numbers, and beginning vocabulary.
- Include them in games on the playground.
- Play student-made vocabulary games with them.
- Listen to taped books with them.
- Walk home with them, or sit with them on the bus.
- Learn a few words of the newcomer's language.

• • • • • • • •

Use cross-grade tutors. Instead of same-age buddies, you may want to try cross-grade tutors or buddies, pairing your newcomers with older students. The ideal situation is to pair older bilingual students and newcomers who speak the same language. The older students can explain classroom procedure and rules to the newcomers. In addition, the buddies can help your students with the newcomer activity pages. Be careful that tutors do not miss too much of their own work.

• • • • • • • •

Incorporate visuals and kinesthetic activities into your teaching. Don't expect students to sit for long periods of time, listening to language that is above their level of comprehension. Try to make the content of your lessons comprehensible, even to the least proficient students. Use gestures, drawings, blackboard sketches, and other visual support. Students in the primary grades can't usually read a dictionary definition in their own language but they can understand a picture from a picture dictionary. Most newcomers respond well to kinesthetic and hands-on activities. Actively engage students in their own learning by involving them in finger plays, pantomime, and other dramatic movement activities.

• • • • • • • •

Use cooperative learning to foster language acquisition. Newcomers who work in cooperative groups have real reasons to learn English. They are an essential part of the class communi-ty and have a contribution to make. Provide meaningful and challenging tasks in English or content–area work at the newcomers' language levels. If cooperative groups in your classroom are working on social studies projects, your new learners of English can do the poster, drawing, or map. They can label, color, paste, fold, cut paper, and be actively involved in a variety of other production and display work. If your class is studying animals, have your newcomers learn the vocabulary from the animal section of the activity pages. A basic understanding of unit vocabulary helps to build self-esteem and may enable the newcomer to contribute to the group project in new ways. Encourage members of the cooperative group to help newcomers learn.

• • • • • • • •

Help your new learners of English develop pride in their home language and culture. Encourage newcomers to share their language skills by teaching classmates to pronounce their home-language words on the labels you have placed around the classroom. Have your newcomers write in a home-language diary, read home-language books, draw pictures of people and places in their home countries, and listen (with headphones) to home-language music. You may want to start a collection of pictures from different countries. Ask bilingual students and parents to bring in home-language maga-zines. Have students cut out pictures and hang them in your room to represent the cultures of your newcomers. When laminated, these pictures can be shared among a number of teachers. Ask bilingual parents to do cultural demonstrations for your class. It is important to encourage the maintenance of home languages and cultures. In addition to helping your newcomers develop a sense of pride in who they are, you are helping them to build schema-ta, skills, and strategies that will eventually transfer into English.

• • • • • • • •

Keep in touch with newcomers' parents. Don't hesitate to write notes home in English. Let parents know how their child is doing. Inform them of problems. Tell them how they can help. (Remember to be realistic in this request.) If parents do not speak English, they will take your note to a friend or relative for translation. It is very effective to communicate with parents in this way. You are guarding their confidentiality by allowing them to choose their own translator. More importantly, you are involving them in their child's education.

· · · · · · · · ·

Keep a list of people in the building who speak the languages of your students. There will be many occasions when you will need someone to translate important instructions. The list of same-language speakers you compile may include other teachers, custodians, same-language students in other classes, and bilingual parent volunteers. For particularly important messages or instructions, you may wish to call on these translators, since kindergartners and first graders are not always the most reliable of translators.

ESTABLISHING AN ESL LEARNING CENTER

Select a corner in your room to be the ESL Learning Center. Set up a small desk or table with several chairs. Use a large box to keep the equipment and materials for your new language learners. Label everything in the Learning Center and organize it so that students, buddies, tutors, and volunteers can easily find what they need. Students can work in this area, or they can carry materials back to their desk. The ESL Student Activity Chart on page 1 should be used and prominently displayed to guide the newcomers and their buddies. Draw pictures or write page numbers on the schedule to show what work you want done. This is especially helpful with second-grade newcomers. Students will feel more comfortable if they know what is expected of them and if their days have purpose.

· · · · · · · · ·

Fill the ESL Learning Center with activities for your new language learners. Here are some of the items you may want to include in your ESL Learning Center. It is not necessary to put everything in at once. Add to the Learning Center a little bit at a time.

◆ tape recorder and earphones
◆ copies of appropriate activity pages from this book (Use these as a Starter Pack [see below], and keep them in a loose-leaf binder, a large envelope, or a folder with pockets.)
◆ crayons, scissors, pencils, erasers, and paper
◆ an ESL notebook
◆ an ESL folder for Dictionary pages (See page T14.)
◆ labels for classroom objects (See pages 3 to 8 and 66 to 69.)
◆ a picture file (class-made or commercial)
◆ well-illustrated magazines for cutting out pictures
◆ blank 3" x 5" index cards to be used for flash cards or concentration games
◆ a picture dictionary
◆ home-language books on your newcomers' reading levels
◆ home-language magazines with lots of pictures

◆ nonfiction picture books from the library that cover the same content material you are currently teaching
◆ beginning phonics books with tapes
◆ taped music in both English and home languages
◆ picture books and well-illustrated beginning-to-read books with tapes
◆ simple games: dot-to-dot activities, word searches, concentration games, sequencing activities, and jigsaw puzzles
◆ an "object" box containing small manipulative objects for beginning vocabulary or phonics learning

· · · · · · · · ·

Make up individualized Starter Packs for your newcomers. Until the newcomer is able to participate in class activities, he or she will need individualized materials to work on. The Starter Pack enables entry-level students to work independently on activities suited to their specific needs. Select appropriate material from the activity pages in this book. Remember, it isn't necessary for students to work through all the pages from beginning to end. Feel free to omit sections or pages that are not appropriate to your students' needs. Reproduce the activity pages and keep them in a large, clearly marked folder. You may wish to three-hole punch the pages so students can keep them neatly in their own binders. Add any other materials that are appropriate for your newcomer. Try to pick activities that can be easily explained to your new language learners.

Encourage students to work on these activities when they cannot follow the work being done in the classroom. You might wish to have students work in the Learning Center as there will be less distraction to the class if newcomers are not cutting and pasting in the middle of your lesson. Remember, however, not to isolate the newcomers from their peers with separate work all day long. They, too, need to be a part of your class and should be integrated as much as possible.

PROVIDING PRODUCTIVE WORK FOR NEWCOMERS

It is a rare newcomer who can "soak up" English by simply sitting in your classroom and listening to your regular instruction. Although they benefit from the social integration of being involved in class activities, it is important to provide newcomers with language opportunities at their ability levels that suit their specific needs. Try to give newcomers regular and appropriate assignments. Be specific and clear in your directions. If your instructions are vague, some students will do nothing. Others will struggle to complete the assignment as given to the rest of the class. Check to be sure that students understand what it is they are to do, particularly during the first several weeks as student work habits are being established. If newcomers are to work productively, it is essential to train them from the beginning to take responsibility for their own learning. Try to both verbally articulate and write instructions as frequently as possible, thus allowing students to link the oral and written languages. Offer materials and opportunities that meet your newcomers' ability levels and needs.

Establish a regular routine for newcomers. At first, everything will be chaotic to your newcomers. Give them help in organizing time, space, and materials. Use the ESL Student Activity Chart on page 1 to give students a sense of structure. Tape it to their desks, or have them keep it at the front of their ESL notebooks. Send a copy home so that parents can help their children feel more connected to the classroom.

Engage newcomers in language learning from the beginning. From the beginning, limited-English-proficient students can be productive in your class. The suggestions that follow are just some of the many ways to actively engage your newcomers in language learning.

◆ COPY WORK Have students copy alphabet letters, numbers, their name, your name, the names of other students in the class, and beginning vocabulary words. Have them draw pictures to demonstrate comprehension of what they are copying.

◆ PERSONALIZED, INTERACTIVE ACTIVITIES Personalize the work from the activity pages. Relate it to what you are doing with the rest of your class. Read the Teacher's Instructions. Many of the activity pages can be interactive if completed with a buddy or volunteer.

◆ ROTE LEARNING While this is not popular in American schools, it is common in many other countries. Parents and students often feel more comfortable if they can see some kind of end product. Don't limit newcomers' learning to rote memorization, but if it comes easily to your students, capitalize on their ability to learn in this manner. Have students use the Dictionary pages in this book to make flash cards. You may also wish to have students learn sight words, poems, chants, songs, lists, and spelling words through rote learning.

◆ THE CLASS AUTHORITY Each newcomer has at least one strength that he or she can share with the class. Make that child the class "authority" in that area. Refer other students to this expert when they need help. Areas of expertise might be computers, math, origami, or art work.

◆ BIG BOOK PICTURE DICTIONARY Staple sheets of 12" x 18" construction paper together and have students cut pictures out of magazines to make a Big Book Picture Dictionary. Divide the book into different categories. Use the categories presented in the newcomer activity pages and add your own to complement your curriculum (for example, a Healthful Foods section to go with your health unit on nutrition). Encourage students to add to the

Dictionary whenever possible. This is an excellent cooperative learning activity that other students can share. Keep the Big Book Picture Dictionary in your ESL Learning Center.

• • • • • • • •

Recruit volunteers to work with newcomers. The activity pages have been designed to accommodate two basic types of learning situations: independent seat work that enables the newcomer to work productively when the teacher is busy with other students, and interactive pair work. To engage students in interactive language learning, simply recruit a buddy, cross-grade tutor, or parent volunteer to work with the newcomer on the activity pages. This is particularly important for newcomers who have just arrived. At first, many students will not speak at all. They will only listen and point. It is

critical to provide students with plenty of aural input in order to familiarize them with the sounds of the English language. Be sure to use a variety of sources for this aural input.

• • • • • • • •

Use recorded material. If a buddy, cross-grade tutor, or parent volunteer is unavailable during class time, you may wish to have them tape materials beforehand. A word of caution, however, about the use of tapes and tape recorders. The student using headphones is isolated from the rest of the class. It is important to limit the use of headphones at first. You may wish to divide the daily listening activities into three or four short segments, according to the age and maturity of each student. If students are literate in their own language, you will want to provide reading and writing instruction along with listening comprehension activities.

TEACHING NEWCOMERS TO READ AND WRITE

Many ESL learners benefit from an environment in which children learn all language skills, including reading and writing, in a natural way. Social inclusion in songs, poetry, drama, chants, and finger plays proves particularly advantageous to the language learner because these activities provide an opportunity for students to learn from their peers. Teaching reading and writing in a literature-rich, theme-based curriculum also benefits newcomers, enabling them to participate on some level in part of the daily instruction, even if it is drawing and labeling a picture.

• • • • • • • •

Read to your newcomers every day. It is important to read to your ESL students on a consistent basis. Supplement your readings with pictures, gestures, and dramatic voice changes to convey meaning. It is helpful to read the same book many times. During the first reading, point to the pictures as you say the corresponding words. In subsequent readings, point to the text as you say each word. Leave out a predictable word as you read the text and allow students the opportunity to provide it. Don't worry if students don't understand every word. It is more important that they have general comprehension of the whole story. When you are reading more difficult books to your entire class, you may wish to ask a bilingual cross-grade tutor or parent volunteer to first explain the story to the newcomers. This will enable them to participate more fully in the readings and follow-up activities you have planned.

• • • • • • • •

Teach newcomers to read in English. Preliterate students and students not familiar with the Roman alphabet will have to start with learning

the names and sounds of the letters. See pages 33 to 47 for beginning alphabet exercises. If you wish to give your students more practice with letter formation and sound-symbol correspondence, you may want to use mainstream materials. As you teach, try to contextualize the phonics as much as possible and bring meaning to what students are learning. Students who have already developed the concept of sound-symbol correspondence in their own language will have a much easier time learning to read in English. Keep in mind that reading is not simply being able to phonetically decode the words on a page, but also being able to construct meaning out of them. Many newcomers learn to decode quite quickly but are unable to understand much of what they read. It is a good idea to constantly check for comprehension.

You can start by teaching your beginning students to say, read, and write:

◆ the letters of the alphabet. Have mainstream or more advanced ESL students teach newcomers the Alphabet Song.

◆ the letters in their name.

- the words *same* and *different*. Once students have mastered these concepts, you can assign exercises that help students distinguish between the shapes and sounds of letters.
- the labels around the room, textbook and subject names, and environmental print.
- basic color, shape, and number words. Use the activity pages in this book. Allow for plenty of repetition and review. Keep the Dictionary pages handy for students to use as a reference.
- the vocabulary from the Dictionary pages of this book. Personalizing the vocabulary will help students to more quickly acquire the English.
- simple stories from books with tapes, either commercial or student-made.

Directions appear on all activity pages. If students are preliterate, or do not know the Roman alphabet, the directions can be read to them. Activity page direction lines can be a useful tool for teaching reading in English.

When your newcomers are reading on their own, choose books that have lots of illustrations with short, predictable text. Books designed for preschool and kindergarten children are appropriate for first- and second-grade newcomers.

Once your students know the alphabet letters and sounds, they can be included in some regular K-2 curriculum work.

● ● ● ● ● ● ● ●
Teach the mechanics of writing the Roman alphabet. Give preliterate students and students not familiar with the Roman alphabet plenty of extra writing practice. Use lined paper that is appropriate to your students' grade and ability. You can find exercises in writing on pages 33 through 41 and 46 to 47. If you wish to give your students more practice with letter formation and small motor coordination, you may want to refer to mainstream materials. If your second-grade class is learning cursive writing, you may wish to include newcomers in these lessons.

● ● ● ● ● ● ● ●
Encourage newcomers to explore creative writing in English. Students will learn to write faster when they have real reasons to write. Many of the activities that you do with your mainstream, bilingual, or ESL students can be adapted for newcomers. Allow them to sequence a story by drawing pictures and labeling with invented spelling. On a piece of paper write sentences from a book they have read and understood; let students draw pictures to go with the sentences. Allow students to retell the story orally in English or in their home language, and have cross-grade tutors or bilingual volunteers write the words down for them. Extend the themes or stories with hands-on activities. Have students make cards or write letters and notes to family members, schoolmates, and friends. Motivate students to write by providing them with meaningful reasons to write.

CREATING OPPORTUNITIES FOR MAINSTREAM STUDENTS AND NEWCOMERS TO WORK TOGETHER

If you are a mainstream classroom teacher, you may be wondering about how to create opportunities for your newcomers to work with your mainstream students. Within the first week, foster social interaction by giving your newcomers classroom jobs just like everyone else. Newcomers can help by distributing handouts, crayons, and napkins; collecting homework and books; and going on short errands. Have your class brainstorm ways to help the new students learn English. Challenge your mainstream students to learn a few words of the newcomer's language. The following are additional ways that you can foster social interaction.

● ● ● ● ● ● ● ●
Compile a picture file. Ask your mainstream students to bring in old magazines. Give all students a category to look for. (This is a good cooperative group or pair activity.) Categories might include food, emotions, family members, sports, transportation, and clothing. Provide time for students to cut out pictures and mount them on oak tag. Have mainstream students neatly write the words for the pictures on the

back. Store the pictures in a cardboard box by category. During their free time, pair student volunteers with newcomers to help them learn the vocabulary words.

● ● ● ● ● ● ● ●
Make vocabulary posters in cooperative groups. Have each group of students cut out pictures from magazines, glue them to large sheets of construction paper or poster board, and label them to create large posters of categories of

common vocabulary words. Categories might be food, clothing, body parts, colors, animals, playground scenes, the family, classroom objects, street scenes, house and furniture, or transportation. Display the posters in your classroom near the ESL Learning Center.

• • • • • • • • •

Make concentration card games. Have English-speaking students create sets of concentration card games for the English-language learners, then play with them during free time or lunch time. Sets may consist of categories such as numbers, colors, shapes, body parts, classroom vocabulary, clothing, food, and animals. Students should choose items that are easy for them to draw, or if they prefer, they can cut pictures out of the Dictionary pages in this book. When students play the concentration games, they should be sure to say the name of the picture out loud to help the newcomers acquire the English vocabulary.

• • • • • • • • •

Make audio tapes. Teach English-speaking classmates or volunteers how to make audio tapes for your new learners of English. Teach buddies or volunteers to speak at a slow but natural pace. Have them use a lot of expression and

normal speaking rhythm. If they are recording the text of a book, have them use a whistle or a bell to let the newcomer know when to turn the page. Here are some things that you, a volunteer, or a mainstream student can record for new English learners.

◆ items that are labeled around the room

◆ the numbers from one to twenty (Use the Number Dictionary on page 22.)

◆ colors, shapes, and classroom direction words (pages 9, 10, and 16)

◆ vocabulary from the Dictionary pages in this book (You may want to number the pictures so that items can be referred to on tape by number.)

◆ the Pledge of Allegiance

◆ the words to a song your class sings at the beginning of the day ("America, the Beautiful")

◆ the Alphabet Song

◆ the text of simple stories

◆ words in a children's picture dictionary (Number the pictures so that students can follow the tape.)

MAKING THE MOST OF BILINGUAL VOLUNTEERS

In the classroom Bilingual volunteers are a great asset to any teacher that works with ESL students at any level. If you are an ESL or bilingual teacher, you may already have a group of parent volunteers who help you in the classroom. If you are a mainstream teacher, you may have limited contact with bilingual parents. Here are some suggestions for starting a Parent Volunteer Program in your school.

• • • • • • • •

Make the initial contact. Contact an approachable parent to ask him or her to help you in your classroom. Don't limit yourself to parents who have children in ESL. Bilingual parents whose children are not in an ESL program often show interest in volunteering to help newcomers. If you are a mainstream teacher, let the ESL teachers in your school know that you are interested in having a parent volunteer work in your room. They will know what languages are spoken in the homes of students in other grades in your school. It is quite possible that the ESL teacher will know the parents and feel comfortable asking them to volunteer. A cultural fair, a food festival, or a program where ESL students will be performing bring a large number of parents into the school and are good events at which you can meet bilingual parents. Parent

conferences offer another avenue through which to recruit volunteers.

• • • • • • • •

Invite parents to help you. Invite parents of different backgrounds to do cultural demonstrations in your classroom. Invite other classes to attend the demonstrations. Some parents may prefer to work one-on-one with students or with small groups of newcomers. Ask parents to let you know in what ways they wish to help.

• • • • • • • •

Welcome all parents. Don't turn anyone away based on language ability. Let limited-English-proficient parents know they are welcome to help you. Parents who do not speak English very well can help you with special projects, act as an extra pair of hands in your classroom, help with a craft project, be an active listener as a student reads, videotape special classroom events, or photocopy materials for your classroom. In addition, older students in your school, senior citizens, high-school students, and community members may wish to help out as well.

• • • • • • • • •

Be prepared for the volunteer. Set up a schedule so that you know when a volunteer is coming. Be prepared for the volunteer; know what work you want him or her to do. You won't have time to do any in-depth training, but any time you spend familiarizing a parent with the materials in the ESL Learning Center, or in using the tape recorder or computer, will be an investment. If the volunteer's English is very limited, ask one of the bilingual parents to train them in their home language. Last year's volunteers can be asked to train this year's. Volunteers should know that you will be busy teaching and won't be able to stop your class to discuss routine details with them. However, it is important to establish and maintain communication with your volunteers. You will want them to inform you of any unusual circumstances that come to their attention. If your time is limited, you may wish to communicate through written notes. Remember to be careful about the kind of information you divulge. Some parents are sensitive about other parents knowing their child's difficulties in school. Be sure to demonstrate your appreciation for the work that volunteers do.

Beyond the classroom As their role expands, these volunteers become more and more invaluable to the school. Bilingual volunteers who speak the same languages as your newcomers are crucial to you not only for the assistance they provide in the classroom but for the services they provide outside the classroom as well. New arrivals and their parents can be relieved of a lot of stress and anxiety by having an adult explain to them in their own language what is expected in American schools.

In addition, bilingual parent volunteers can:

◆ become a liaison between a new family and the school.

◆ help new arrivals with registration, inoculation and health records, etc.

◆ give new arrivals a tour of the school.

◆ support the classroom teacher both affectively and with instruction. In the beginning of the school year, a volunteer's role may be primarily affective. Later many bilingual volunteers take on instructional roles, helping students with content-area work.

◆ explain to new parents American school programs, which may be very different from those in their home countries. Parents new to this country have a difficult time understanding the concepts of whole language, cooperative learning, invented spelling, thinking skills activities, and manipulatives in math. A poor understanding of the American educational system can lead to a lack of confidence in the system.

◆ help establish a telephone chain for notifying families about emergency school closings and for relaying important messages from the school to the home.

◆ help special-subject teachers, administrators, and the school nurse if there is a problem with a limited-English-proficient student.

◆ take an active role in educating teachers, students, and administrators about their home culture. Bilingual parents can present a cultural program at a staff in-service day. They can also teach students and staff about their language and culture through participation in cultural activities in the school.

◆ teach useful phrases in their language to teachers.

◆ interpret during parent-teacher conferences.

◆ translate school correspondence: letters, report cards, messages, notes to parents.

◆ help with "sensitive" issues: retention, referral, social problems, and so on.

Everyone gains from the participation of bilingual parent volunteers in a school: the school benefits from an increase in the quality of communication with the parents of their language-minority population; the classroom teacher gets extra help with students; the students benefit from the cultural input of the bilingual parents; newcomers benefit both socially and academically; and the parents of newcomers are relieved of much anxiety about their children. Bilingual volunteers reap benefits as well, as their self-esteem and pride in their culture grow. They may feel more comfortable in the school and often develop friendships with the teachers they help.

TIPS ON COMMUNICATING

☑ When you communicate with newcomers, it is important to continually provide them with **comprehensible input**, that is, language that is accessible to students. Use drawings, gestures, actions, emotions, voice variety, chalkboard sketches, photographs, and visual materials to provide clues to meaning. Adding kinesthetic movements to support the language will provide additional comprehensible input.

☑ Smile and keep a friendly expression on your face.

☑ Talk at a slow-to-normal pace, in short sentences. Use a pleasant tone.

☑ Be patient. Demonstrate this patience through your facial expression and body language.

☑ Use simple sentence structure (subject-verb-object).

☑ Use high-frequency words.

☑ Use names of people rather than pronouns.

☑ Pause after phrases or short sentences, not after each word. You do not want to distort the rhythm of the language.

☑ Be willing to repeat your message using the same simple words and simple sentence structures, actions, or demonstrations.

☑ If you have something important to convey, speak one-on-one to the newcomer rather than in front of the class. The anxiety of being in the spotlight interferes with comprehension.

☑ Talk in a calm, quiet manner. Talking louder sounds angry and does not increase comprehension.

☑ Avoid using the passive voice and complex sentences.

☑ When possible, use a bilingual dictionary for words that cannot be drawn or acted out. If your students can't read, ask a bilingual student or parent volunteer to translate.

☑ Resist the urge to overcorrect errors in speaking. This will cause anxiety and reduce efforts to speak. Give indirect correction by repeating what the student said in correct English.

☑ Encourage new learners of English to act out or to draw pictures to get their meaning across. Show patience; don't jump in immediately to supply the words for the student.

☑ Encourage mainstream students to allow your new learners of English "translation time" when listening and speaking. Explain that newcomers are translating the language they hear back to their home language, formulating a response, and then translating that response into English.

☑ Accept one-word answers.

☑ Ask simple yes/no and either/or questions so that newcomers have an opportunity to respond.

☑ If the student response is heavily accented, repeat it correctly. Do not ask the student to repeat. This can be very embarrassing.

☑ Include assignments that allow students to share knowledge of their culture and country with the class. Work will be more meaningful if students feel connected to the subject matter.

K-2 Newcomer Program

INSTRUCTIONS FOR
NEWCOMER ACTIVITY PAGES

▲▼▲

ESL Student Activity Chart

APPLICATIONS: To manage newcomers' instruction ◆ To give direction and structure to the newcomers' school day ◆ To foster students' comfort in the classroom by setting clear academic expectations

INSTRUCTIONS: This management tool for teachers is easily followed by beginning students, bilingual volunteers, and cross-grade tutors. Photocopy this page each week and put it in the Learning Center or at the front of the students' notebooks. Each day, write page numbers or draw a picture in each box to communicate the activities that you want students to complete.

ESL Learning Center Sign

APPLICATION: To help students keep their materials organized

OBJECTIVE: To make a sign

INSTRUCTIONS: Make several copies of the sign. Have students color in the letters. Tape the signs onto the sides and the top of the box that you are using to store Learning Center materials. See Establishing an ESL Learning Center on page T6.

Classroom Labels

APPLICATIONS: To create a supportive classroom environment ◆ To provide a means for establishing rapport with newcomers ◆ To enable newcomers to share their home language

OBJECTIVES: To acquire classroom vocabulary ◆ To associate spoken language with print

INSTRUCTIONS: Photocopy a complete set of labels for each different language spoken in your classroom. Ask a native speaker to write each word in the home language below the English word. Have students tape the labels to the appropriate places in the classroom. Most newcomers will recognize their home language and feel proud to see it displayed in the classroom.

To preserve the labels, glue each one to a large index card or piece of oak tag. Laminate the labels after the home-language translations have been completed. File the labels when you are not using them so that they can be copied for new arrivals in the future.

Classroom Directions

APPLICATIONS: To provide a reference page for students when they are completing the activity pages ◆ To help students recognize classroom direction words

INSTRUCTIONS: Explain or act out each word on the page. Have students keep this page at the front of their ESL notebooks. If students are literate in their own language, have classmates of the same language write translations. Newcomers will learn the words over time and through usage. Encourage them to look for direction words each time they begin a new activity page.

Color Chart . . . . Page 10

APPLICATION: To provide a reference page for students when they are completing coloring activities

OBJECTIVE: To match colors to color words

INSTRUCTIONS: Provide the needed crayons for students to color the reference page. Encourage students to find the color word on each crayon and match it to the corresponding word on the chart. For kindergartners and new first graders, have students begin with four colors and gradually add new color words to their vocabulary.

Coloring Activities . . . . Pages 11–14

OBJECTIVES: To demonstrate recognition of color words ◆ To name and identify colors ◆ To practice writing color words

INSTRUCTIONS: Have students color as directed. Ask them to say the words as they color. Call out the colors, and have newcomers point to the color you name. Have first- and second-grade students practice writing the color words on a sheet of paper that is lined appropriately for their grade level.

Draw 2 Yellow Bananas . . . . Page 15

OBJECTIVES: To practice reading color and direction words ◆ To associate pictures with spoken words

INSTRUCTIONS: If necessary, review the numbers one through seven. Then introduce the words for the pictures by pointing to each illustration, naming it, and having students repeat after you. Next, help students read the sentences aloud. Have them draw pictures and color as directed. Review the page by asking students to point to two yellow bananas, five green trees, etc.

Dictionary Pages . . . . Pages 16; 22; 50–51; 83–84; 94–95; 103–105; 119–122; 131–132; 159–162

APPLICATION: To provide reference pages for each of the vocabulary clusters treated in this book

OBJECTIVE: To acquire basic vocabulary

INSTRUCTIONS: Say each word in English and have students repeat after you. Have a bilingual cross-grade tutor or bilingual parent volunteer write a translation next to each dictionary entry for those newcomers who are literate in their home language. Ask students to point to each item on the page as you name it. For those students who seem ready, indicate an item and ask, "What is this?" Students who are ready to read and write can use the Dictionary pages as a basis for reading and writing activities. Have second-grade students copy the words into their ESL notebooks, translate them, and write a sentence with each word.

When using the Number Dictionary on page 22, call students' attention to the two sets of numbers presented here. Point out that numbers that appear on a book page, or are typeset (those which appear in the left columns), are formed differently from numbers which students write (those which students are asked to trace). In particular, call out the differences between the typeset and handwritten 4, 8, and 9.

You may wish to provide students with a folder for keeping their Dictionary pages. Organizing the pages in this way will enable them to more easily refer to the Dictionaries during other activities.

EXTENSION: Make several copies of each Dictionary page. Use the vocabulary to create concentration or bingo games, flash cards, labels for pictures and bulletin board displays, and so forth.

Color the Shapes . . . . Pages 17–19

OBJECTIVES: To identify and name common shapes ◆ To follow directions involving shape and color words

INSTRUCTIONS: Review each shape by pointing to a picture of it on the page and saying the word. Then have students point to the correct picture as you call out a shape name. As students begin to relate the picture to the spoken word, point to a shape and ask, "What is this?" Read aloud the directions for all students.

Circle, Rectangle, or Square? . . . . Pages 20–21

OBJECTIVES: To categorize objects by shape ◆ To associate objects with common shapes

INSTRUCTIONS: Have students color and cut out the pictures on page 20. Show them how to sort the pictures into groups of objects with similar shapes. Then have them put the pictures in the correct columns on page 21. For nonreaders, draw a picture of each shape next to the heading.

EXTENSION: Help more advanced students learn the names of the objects on page 20 and write a short sentence about each picture. ("This is a circle. The door is a rectangle.")

Match the Numbers . . . . Pages 23–26

OBJECTIVES: To count from one to twenty in English ◆ To match numbers to number words

INSTRUCTIONS: Have students practice counting from one to twenty in English with a buddy, cross-grade tutor, or parent volunteer. Help students to use the Number Dictionary on page 22 as they work on this activity. Newcomers may have more success with these pages if they work from the center out, first counting the number of items in a given picture and then drawing lines to the number and number word. Teach students to cross out items as they count.

Missing Numbers . . . . Pages 27–28

OBJECTIVE: To identify and write missing numbers (0–20)

INSTRUCTIONS: Help students to refer to the Number Dictionary on page 22 as they fill in the missing numbers. When students have completed page 27, you may wish to have them read aloud the numbers from zero to twenty. Provide extra practice in writing numbers for those students who need it.

EXTENSION: Buddies or cross-grade tutors may enjoy creating missing number examples like those on page 28 for newcomers to complete.

Find the Fish . . . . Page 29

OBJECTIVE: To match numbers to number words

INSTRUCTIONS: Show students how to cut along the dotted lines and match each tail to the correct fish. Provide students with glue to attach the tails.

Draw Ten Kites . . . . Page 30

OBJECTIVES: To demonstrate an understanding of number words ◆ To practice reading number words

INSTRUCTIONS: You may wish to first teach the words for the pictures by pointing to the illustrations, saying each word, and having students repeat after you. Next, help students read the sentences aloud. Have them draw the number of pictures indicated. Review the page by asking students to point to ten kites, four sharks, etc.

Number Words . . . . Pages 31–32

OBJECTIVES: To write number words in order, from zero to twenty ◆ To match numbers to number words

INSTRUCTIONS: Help students to use the Number Dictionary on page 22 and the number words at the top of the page to complete the first activity. Read page 31 with newcomers who are not yet comfortable writing in English, and ask them to find the missing word at the top of the page and point to it. You may wish to have students who are preliterate or unfamiliar with the Roman alphabet work on this page after they have done the alphabet activities on pages 33 to 47 of this book.

EXTENSIONS: Have a buddy, cross-grade tutor, or volunteer dictate a list of numbers to the newcomer. Instruct beginning students to write the numbers and second graders to write number words. You might also suggest that students make number/number-word concentration games to play with newcomers.

The Alphabet . . . . Pages 33–36

OBJECTIVES: To learn the names of the letters in the Roman alphabet ◆ To practice writing upper- and lowercase letters

INSTRUCTIONS: (The alphabet activities in this book have been designed for preliterate newcomers and those students who are not familiar with the Roman alphabet.) You may wish to introduce students to the English alphabet by having them repeat the letters as you read them aloud. Next, have students practice the formation of each letter, first by tracing the letters with a finger, then by writing them in the spaces provided. Kindergarten students may need to practice first on a large surface such as a chalkboard. Have students say the letters as they write them on the alphabet pages. For further practice with the formation of letters, have students work on ruled paper that is appropriate to their grade level.

Alphabet Dictionary . . . . Pages 37–41

OBJECTIVES: To associate letters of the alphabet with words that begin with those letters ◆ To copy words ◆ To recognize sound-symbol correspondence ◆ To match upper- and lowercase letters

INSTRUCTIONS: (These exercises are particularly useful for preliterate students and those newcomers who are not familiar with the Roman alphabet.) Read aloud the letters of the alphabet and demonstrate their sounds through the dictionary words provided. Have students repeat the words after you and then write them in the spaces. Ask students to match the upper- and lowercase letters in the exercises at the bottom of each page. You may want to have students copy the vocabulary words into their ESL notebooks. For those newcomers literate in their home language, have a bilingual cross-grade tutor or bilingual parent volunteer write a home-language translation for each entry. Remind students to keep all of their Dictionary pages together in a folder. Although these exercises have been designed for students who are learning the Roman alphabet, all students may benefit from copying words and compiling their own Dictionary pages.

K-2 Newcomer Program

Letters, Letters . . . . Pages 42–43

OBJECTIVE: To discriminate between letters of the alphabet

INSTRUCTIONS: (These exercises are for preliterate students and those newcomers who are not familiar with the Roman alphabet.) Have students circle the first letter in each row and then the letters in the row that are the same. For students who need additional practice in distinguishing letters of the alphabet, have cross-grade tutors or volunteers design pages with exercises similar to those presented here.

Find the Engine . . . . Page 44

OBJECTIVES: To practice discriminating between lowercase *d, b, p,* and *q* ◆ To match these letters with their uppercase counterparts

INSTRUCTIONS: (These exercises are for preliterate students and those newcomers who are not familiar with the Roman alphabet.) Have students cut out the train cars and arrange them behind the four engines. Then point first to the engine and then to each car, asking, "What letter is this?" If appropriate, help children check the Alphabet Dictionary (pages 37–41) to make sure their selections are correct. When all of the cars are sorted and matched to the engines, have children glue them in place.

Alphabet Match . . . . Page 45

OBJECTIVE: To match upper- and lowercase letters

INSTRUCTIONS: (These exercises are for preliterate students and those newcomers who are not familiar with the Roman alphabet.) Have students draw a line from each uppercase letter to the corresponding lowercase letter. Cross-grade tutors or volunteers can show students how to use the Alphabet Dictionary (pages 37–41) to check their work.

Write the Missing Letters . . . . Page 46

OBJECTIVE: To write letters in alphabetical order

INSTRUCTIONS: (These exercises are for preliterate students and those newcomers who are not familiar with the Roman alphabet.) Make several copies of this page so that students can do the activity as many times as necessary. Have students fill in the missing letters. Teach them how to refer to the alphabet at the top of the page. When newcomers have completed this page, have them try it without the aid of the alphabet chart. (Photocopy the page with the chart covered.)

EXTENSION: Have cross-grade tutors or volunteers make similar pages with different letters missing.

ABC Order . . . . Page 47

OBJECTIVE: To practice arranging letters in ABC order

INSTRUCTIONS: (These exercises are for preliterate students and those newcomers who are not familiar with the Roman alphabet.) Using the first example, show students how to put the letters in the correct alphabetical order. Demonstrate how to use the alphabet chart at the top of the page.

EXTENSION: Use this page to teach how to alphabetize words. Have students write the words from the Alphabet Dictionary (pages 37–41) on small pieces of paper. Help them find the words that correspond to the four alphabet letters in the first example (*jacket, house, ice, game*). Have students alphabetize the words just as they did the letters (*game, house, ice, jacket*). Continue in the same way with the remaining examples on the page.

What Is the Date? . . . . Page 48

OBJECTIVES: To name the days of the week ◆ To complete a calendar page for the current month

INSTRUCTIONS: Have students practice the pronunciation of the days of the week. To establish meaning for the different days, point out the days on which they come to school. Many cultures begin the week with Monday rather than Sunday. It is important that students understand this difference or the calendar will be distorted for them. Have them fill in the calendar for the current month and write the name of the month at the top. Depending on their age and ability level, have students practice concepts such as, "Today is Wednesday. Tomorrow is Thursday. Yesterday was Tuesday."

EXTENSIONS: Make copies of this calendar for student use during the months they are in your class. As the students gain in language ability, ask more difficult questions, such as, "What day is gym?" "What date is the third Thursday of the month?" The calendar can also be used to keep a record of the dates of holidays and the days for special activities, or to make a weather calendar.

Days of the Week . . . . Page 49

OBJECTIVE: To write the days of the week in order

INSTRUCTIONS: Before children begin writing, have them name the days of the week in order. To render the activity more challenging, fold over the page to cover the days of the week at the top and/or the first letter in each example.

Which Month Is Next? . . . . Page 52

OBJECTIVE: To write the months of the year in order

INSTRUCTIONS: Have students recite the months in order. Then have them write the names of the months in order, using the Months of the Year Dictionary on pages 50 and 51. Encourage second graders and students who are more proficient in English to do the activity without the help of the Dictionary.

Sequencing Activities . . . . Pages 53–54; 114–115; 168–169

OBJECTIVES: To arrange a set of pictures in a logical sequence ◆ To demonstrate an understanding of spoken language

INSTRUCTIONS: Go over each picture with students, discussing what comes first, second, etc. Have students color and cut out the pictures. Help them arrange the pictures in order. Then use the pictures to tell a simple story. A short sentence for each picture is sufficient. For example, on page 114 you might begin with, "The girl is looking at the snow." Review the page by using language from the story. For page 114 you might ask students to point to the picture of the girl looking at the snow. Keep in mind that some of the sequencing activities are culture-bound and students will need to depend fully on the logic of the picture clues to determine the correct order. Students who have never seen snow, for instance, will have no personal experience in making a snowman (pages 53 and 54).

EXTENSION: As students become more proficient in English, they will be able to use these pages as a basis for telling stories orally to a buddy, cross-grade tutor, or parent volunteer, and for writing short sentences about each picture.

What Comes Next? . . . . Pages 55–56

OBJECTIVE: To put months of the year in order

INSTRUCTIONS: Have students recite the months of the year in order as they arrange the pictures. Suggest that students refer to the Months of the Year Dictionary on pages 50 and 51 if they need help.

EXTENSION: Have same-language cross-grade tutors or bilingual parent volunteers talk with newcomers about the different types of weather, activities, and holidays in a particular month in their home culture and then compare it with where they now live in the United States.

Word Search Activities . . . . Pages 57; 73; 91; 111; 128; 157; 170

OBJECTIVES: To use visual discrimination skills ◆ To find new vocabulary words hidden in a puzzle

INSTRUCTIONS: Have students search the puzzle horizontally, vertically, and diagonally to find the words listed at the top of the page. Students who have never done this type of activity may need help with their first puzzle. Encourage students to cross out words at the top of the page as they find them in the puzzle. Students may enjoy pointing out other familiar words that they find.

Where Is the Cat? (Dictionary) . . . . Pages 58–59

OBJECTIVES: To use place prepositions ◆ To demonstrate an understanding of spatial relationships

INSTRUCTIONS: These are the dictionary pages for eight place prepositions: *in, under, on, next to, over, in front of, behind,* and *between.* Introduce these concepts using small objects (a toy cat and a paper bag if you have them). Teach the vocabulary words *cat* and *bag.* Then have newcomers cut out and glue each picture on an index card. Place all the cards face up on the table. Ask students to point to the picture that shows "The cat is in the bag." Practice all of the prepositions in this way until students identify the pictures correctly. Next, point to a picture and ask, "Where is the cat?" At first students need only reply with a phrase such as, "in the bag." As children become more confident in their use of these concepts, ask them to tell you about a picture. Encourage them to respond with sentences. Offer an example such as, "The cat is in the bag." This is a good activity to have a cross-grade tutor or bilingual parent volunteer do with the newcomer.

It is important to remember that place prepositions are not easily translated from language to language. If students already understand these concepts in their home language, learning how to articulate them in English will be easier. Kindergartners and other newcomers learning about spatial relationships for the first time will need a lot of practice with these concepts.

Photocopy another set of these pages for students to add to their folder for Dictionary pages.

Where Is the . . . ? Activity Pages . . . . Pages 60–63

OBJECTIVE: To demonstrate an understanding of spatial relationships and place prepositions

INSTRUCTIONS: Read each sentence with the students. Help them cut out and glue the animals from the bottom of the pages in the correct places. Encourage students to refer to the place preposition dictionary on pages 58 and 59. On pages 61 and 62, show students how to cut along the dotted lines in the pictures and insert the animals "behind" the objects.

OBJECTIVE: To demonstrate an understanding of spatial relationships and place prepositions

INSTRUCTIONS: Have students draw a line from each box on the left to the box on the right that illustrates the same spatial relationship. Encourage students to read aloud the prepositional phrase in each sentence ("under the hive", "under the bag").

OBJECTIVES: To acquire basic vocabulary ◆ To associate pictures with spoken words
  ◆ To relate speech to print

INSTRUCTIONS: Have students color, cut out, and then glue the pictures to index cards or to 3" x 5" pieces of oak tag. Glue the name of the object on the back of each card for children who are at the earliest stages of language acquisition. (Have students who are beginning to recognize sound-symbol correspondence help you match the pictures to the words before you attach them to the index cards. Say a word and allow students the opportunity to use their understanding of initial letters and sounds or consonant sounds to identify the correct written form.) Choose the vocabulary words that are relevant to your students. For the classroom flash cards, if a particular vocabulary word is expressed differently in your school, write it on the back of the card (for example, *blackboard* instead of *chalkboard*). To introduce newcomers to the vocabulary, point to pictures and have the students repeat the words. Place six to twelve of the cards, depending on the students' age and ability level, picture-side up. Ask the students to point to a particular item. Practice until students can identify the correct cards. Then point to a picture and ask, "What is this?" At first, students need only reply with a phrase such as, "a pencil." When students become more proficient in English, ask them to reply with a complete sentence.

Photocopy another set of these pages for students to add to their folder for Dictionary pages.

EXTENSION: As you hold up a picture, have second-grade students refer to a vocabulary list and write the appropriate word. As they develop more language ability, students may be able to write the words without using the list.

OBJECTIVES: To demonstrate aural or reading comprehension of new vocabulary
  ◆ To write new vocabulary words

INSTRUCTIONS: Have students draw pictures of the items indicated. Read each example aloud for nonreaders. Then ask students to copy the boldface words in the spaces provided. Finally, have students color the objects. If you wish to gauge how much of the vocabulary students can read, have them work on their own.

OBJECTIVES: To use numerical and alphabetical order to complete a picture
  ◆ To develop ability to predict

INSTRUCTIONS: All of the dot-to-dot activities in this book use letters of the alphabet or number words. Ask students to guess what the picture is. Review the alphabet or number words at the top of the page. Read the directions aloud, and connect the first few dots with the students. After students have completed the dot-to-dot picture, have them name what they have drawn. Help them find the correct spelling of the word on the corresponding Dictionary or flash card pages (pages 66–69, 103–105, 140–145, 159–162, respectively) and then write it below the picture.

K-2 Newcomer Program

ABC Order Activities . . . . Pages 74–75; 116–117; 129–130

OBJECTIVES: To practice writing and spelling new vocabulary words ◆ To alphabetize words

INSTRUCTIONS: Read the list of words with the students. Show them how to use the alphabet chart at the top of the page to help them write the words correctly in ABC order. When correctly alphabetized, the words will match the pictures.

You may wish to use a different approach with beginning students. Ask them to identify each picture. If they are able, have them point to the word that represents each picture and then copy the word. When they have completed the page, point out that the words are in ABC order.

One or More? . . . . Page 76

OBJECTIVES: To sort pictures into sets of *one* and *more than one* ◆ To use singular and plural nouns

INSTRUCTIONS: Elicit from students the vocabulary words shown in the pictures. Introduce the plural forms of each item, and have students repeat them after you. Help children cut out and then sort the pictures into piles of one and more than one. After students have glued the items in place, give them the opportunity to practice using the singular and plural forms. Point to each picture and elicit "one ruler," "two flags," etc.

EXTENSION: As second-grade students become more proficient in English, give them a word list of the items shown on this page. Have them write the words below the correct headings. For more advanced students, you might add some other vocabulary words and their plurals (*map, maps; chair, chairs*).

In or On? . . . . Pages 77–78

OBJECTIVES: To demonstrate an understanding of classroom vocabulary, place prepositions, and color words ◆ To follow directions to complete a drawing

INSTRUCTIONS: Look at the picture. Review the classroom vocabulary with students, having them point to various objects. Read aloud with students the directions at the top of page 78 and in Part A. Be sure they understand that they are to use the picture on page 77 and then complete each sentence by circling the correct word. For each example, have students first find the classroom object in the picture on page 77. Then ask an either/or question, allowing students the opportunity to respond using a prepositional phrase. For instance, in the first example ask students, "Are the books *in the table* or *on the table?*" After children have responded orally, show them how to circle the correct answer. Say the correct sentence and have students repeat it. You may wish to allow

beginning readers and more proficient students the opportunity to complete the rest of the sentences on their own. Some students may need help identifying the classroom object in question in each of the sentences (books, glue, crayons, etc.).

In Part B, read aloud the directions for nonreaders.

EXTENSION: Have students draw a picture of their classroom. Encourage them to include as many classroom objects as possible. Help them label the objects. Ask younger students questions to elicit the use of place prepositions and classroom vocabulary. Have second graders write sentences describing their picture. ("The crayons are on the floor.")

OBJECTIVES: To write his or her name in English ◆ To develop pride in home-language names and cultures

INSTRUCTIONS: Many students have their name changed by their parents or the school office when they enter a school in the United States. These pages provide students with the opportunity to feel proud of their home-language name and culture. Have students read the title and then color the larger words. Use a bilingual buddy or volunteer, if necessary, to ask them if their name has changed in any way.

As you work with students, you may find it helpful to use the reference numbers on the activity pages. They have been numbered to correspond to the directions here.

Have students:

1. write their birth or given name as they do in the United States.
2. write their family name as they do in the United States.
3. write their whole name as they do in the United States.

4. write the name of their home language (example: Korean, Chinese, Indian, Mexican). Spell the words that they will need.
5. write their name as they do in their home language, using their native alphabet. Tell them to include any names that are dropped in English, such as a two-part first name.
6. write the name of their home language again.
7. write their family name as they do in their home language. Remind them to include any names that are dropped in English, such as a two-part family name.
8. write the name of their country. Remember that they may not know how to say or spell it in English.
9. write their whole name exactly as they do in their home language.

Display these pages in your classroom to share with other students.

OBJECTIVES: To become acquainted with the people and places in the new school environment ◆ To name people and places at school

INSTRUCTIONS: Teach the vocabulary on pages 81 and 82, using the pictures to aid you. If possible, have a bilingual cross-grade tutor or parent volunteer write home-language translations on the page for newcomers. Ask classmates to take the new students around your school and locate the places mentioned here. Have newcomers write the names of the people in your school. Suggest that students color these pages. Hang them up in your classroom.

EXTENSIONS: Have the rest of the class brainstorm other important locations in your school, such as the cafeteria, auditorium, or bus drop-off. Make new pages for these places.

Have students draw a picture of their home-country school. Ask bilingual volunteers to help students label the picture, both in their home language and in English.

OBJECTIVES: To identify parts of the body ◆ To match pictures to written words ◆ To write the names of the parts of the body

INSTRUCTIONS: Have students point to the different parts of the body as you name them. Read the words below the picture with the students. Ask questions such as, "Where is the head?" Have students cut out each word and glue it in the correct place. Second-grade students may want to write the names in the boxes instead of cutting and gluing.

My Face
Page 87

OBJECTIVES: To label a drawing ◆ To write or name parts of the head

INSTRUCTIONS: Have students each draw a picture of their head and label it using the vocabulary at the top of the page. If appropriate, do one or two labels with the group as a model. Preliterate students may need to dictate the names of the parts of the head to you or to a cross-grade tutor. Have newcomers share their drawings with other students in the class.

Read, Match, and Write Activities
Pages 88–89; 98–99

OBJECTIVES: To match pictures to print ◆ To write vocabulary words

INSTRUCTIONS: Read the words in the left-hand column with students. Show students how to use the Parts of the Body Dictionary on pages 83 and 84 (or the Action Word Dictionary on pages 94 and 95) to find the meaning of each word. Have students draw a line from each word to the correct picture. Then, using the example, demonstrate how to write the vocabulary word on the line beside the picture. It may make it clearer to some students to draw a line from the picture to the corresponding write-on-line before they write the word.

How Many Toes Do You Have?
Page 90

OBJECTIVES: To demonstrate an understanding of words that name parts of the body ◆ To write number words

INSTRUCTIONS: Review the number words with students before they begin the activity. Help students to understand the task at hand by doing the first item with them. Have students identify the body part word in the sentence, and then ask them to point to their toes. Ask students how many toes they have. Show them how to write the number word on the line. If necessary, use a yellow highlighter to mark the body part names in the rest of the sentences. Refer students to the Parts of the Body Dictionary on pages 83 and 84 if they need help. You may wish to do this activity orally with kindergartners and some first graders.

A Make-Believe Monster—1
Page 92

OBJECTIVES: To identify parts of the body ◆ To follow directions for coloring a picture

INSTRUCTIONS: Using the picture of the monster, have students point to the body parts as you ask questions such as, "Where are the monster's hands?" Generate one- or two-word responses by asking questions such as, "How many hands does it have?" Have students color the picture according to the directions.

A Make-Believe Monster—2
Page 93

OBJECTIVE: To demonstrate comprehension of number words and words that name parts of the body

INSTRUCTIONS: You may wish to do the first two examples with students to make sure that they understand the directions. Ask students, "Does the monster have two feet?" as you point to the picture on page 92. When they respond affirmatively, explain that a "yes" response means that they circle the picture on page 93. Ask if the monster has three tails. Demonstrate that a "no" response means that they put an "X" on the picture. Readers can do the page independently once they understand the directions. Read each question to nonreaders.

Write the Missing Letters Pages 96–97

OBJECTIVES: To identify pictured actions ◆ To associate words with pictures ◆ To practice spelling action words

INSTRUCTIONS: Have students look at each picture and name the action they think is represented. Help students find the action word in the Action Word Dictionary on pages 94 and 95. Show them how to compare the dictionary word with the incomplete action word on the activity page and fill in the missing letters. Review the page by calling out an action and having students point to the correct picture.

EXTENSION: Cut out pictures of action words and put them on cards. Show a picture to a volunteer. Have him or her mime the action and invite others to guess what he or she is doing. This is an activity in which class buddies can participate.

What Can You Do? Page 100

OBJECTIVES: To demonstrate an understanding of action words and classroom vocabulary ◆ To complete a written sentence using an action word

INSTRUCTIONS: Review the vocabulary words at the top of the page along with the classroom vocabulary words used in the sentences. If students need assistance as they work, mime an action to elicit the answer. Help beginning readers identify the written form through sound-symbol correspondence. Ask students to copy the sentences in their ESL notebooks.

Action or Thing? Pages 101–102

OBJECTIVE: To classify words as "things" (nouns) and "actions" (verbs)

INSTRUCTIONS: Read aloud the definitions and examples on page 101. Have students mime the action words with you and touch the classroom objects. Repeat the words *do* and *touch* as you point to the pictures of the girl reading and the table, respectively. Provide other examples of action words and things, using vocabulary that has already been taught. If students need help with the exercise at the bottom of the page, ask them to tell you which pictures they can act out. Be sure they understand that they are to circle the actions and underline the things.

On page 102, you might suggest that students sort the pictures into two piles before they begin to glue them down. Remind them that actions are things they can *do*.

EXTENSION: Compile a list of twenty common action words that are relevant to your students and classroom (wave, sing, laugh, sneeze, jump, etc.). Teach students to respond to each word with a specific movement or action. For example, when you call out "wave," have students respond by waving their hands in the air. When each action word has been assigned an action and students are beginning to respond correctly, play a game with them. Have students stand in a circle. Call out an action word, or a series of action words, and have students respond without speaking. For instance, "Sneeze, jump" would elicit a sneeze and then a jump from the students.

What's Different? Page 110

OBJECTIVES: To identify the item that does not belong in a set ◆ To name categories for sets of related pictures

INSTRUCTIONS: Have students name the items in each row and then point to the item that does not belong. Be sure they understand that they are to mark an "X" on each item that does not belong in the row. Have students tell how the other four items are related. Students may wish to color the sets of related pictures.

Cut and Match Categorizing Activities . . . . Pages 112–113; 125–126; 136–137; 155–156; 166

OBJECTIVES: To sort illustrated words into categories ◆ To review vocabulary

INSTRUCTIONS: Review the vocabulary on the page with students, having them point to the pictures as you name the items. Point to the headings, and read them aloud. Demonstrate the meaning of the headings, using mime, gestures, or pictures. Have students color, cut out, and then glue the pictures below the correct heading. Review by asking students to point to or name the correct heading as you call out the vocabulary words.

EXTENSION: Write the headings at the top of a piece of construction paper. Have students draw or cut out from magazines pictures of other items that relate to each heading. For example, on the student-made chart for pages 155 and 156, children may draw a backpack or glue a picture of a board game below the Closet heading. Encourage students to include items not listed in the Dictionaries or presented in the flash card activities. Help students to label pictures. Have second graders write a sentence for each picture by providing them with a model, such as "I keep _____ in the closet." You may want to have students glue their labeled pictures on the appropriate pages in the Big Book Picture Dictionary (see pages T7–T8).

Crossword Puzzles . . . . Pages 118; 158; 171

OBJECTIVES: To solve a crossword puzzle using picture clues ◆ To practice spelling vocabulary words

INSTRUCTIONS: (These activities have been designed for second graders and students in the second half of first grade. Younger children may enjoy working on the puzzles as well but may need more directed and continuous support.) Go over the picture clues at the bottom of the page. Have students identify each item and then refer to the corresponding Dictionary or flash card pages (pages 103–105, 140–145, 159–162, respectively) to check the spelling of the words. Suggest that students write the name of each item next to its picture or on a piece of paper with the puzzle number. Show students how to write the correct word in the puzzle spaces. Teach students to count the number of letters in a word in the event that a clue is not clear or a word does not fit. Do not assume that students have had experience with crossword puzzles in their own language.

Where Does it Go? . . . . Pages 123–124

OBJECTIVES: To sort illustrated words into categories ◆ To sort furniture by room

INSTRUCTIONS: For each page, review with students the vocabulary at the bottom and the two category headings. Have students point to each picture as you call out its name. Ask students to determine the room in which each piece of furniture belongs. Have students color, cut out, and then glue the pictures below the correct heading.

EXTENSION: Write the name of each room at the top of a piece of construction paper. Have students draw or cut out magazine pictures of other items that are found in each room. For instance, under "Bathroom" students might include pictures of towels, toothpaste, and toothbrushes. More proficient students may be able to write the names of such items. Help students to label pictures.

Inside or Outside? . . . . Page 127

OBJECTIVES: To name outside parts of a house ◆ To classify items as belonging either inside or outside of a house

INSTRUCTIONS: Review the *inside* vocabulary and teach the *outside* vocabulary by having students repeat each word after you as you point to the picture. Point out the crayons, and read aloud the directions. Have students identify the items as belonging either inside or outside of a house and then color the pictures accordingly. Review the vocabulary by asking students to point to the correct picture as you call out each word.

What Goes Together? . . . . Pages 135; 152–154

OBJECTIVES: To sort illustrated words into categories ◆ To review vocabulary

INSTRUCTIONS: Review the vocabulary on the page by having students point to an object as you name it. Be sure they understand that they are to color, cut out, and then glue the pictures in the correct squares. You might wish to help students first identify and name the four different categories on the page. More proficient students may be able to sort the pictures on their own and then name the category.

Is the Doll in the Toy Box? . . . . Pages 138–139

OBJECTIVES: To demonstrate an understanding of place prepositions and newly acquired vocabulary ◆ To answer questions about a picture

INSTRUCTIONS: Use page 138 to review toy vocabulary and place prepositions with the students. Read the questions on page 139 with students and have them identify the toy vocabulary word in each sentence. (In some cases, the subject is a clothing word instead.) You may wish to highlight the words with a yellow marker for beginning readers. Ask children to find the toy in the picture. Then read the question again and have students mark the correct answers. You may wish to do the entire activity aloud with nonreaders.

What Do You Like to Eat? . . . . Page 150

OBJECTIVES: To express food likes and dislikes ◆ To sort illustrated food words into categories according to preference

INSTRUCTIONS: Review the vocabulary on the page with students. Demonstrate the meaning of "I like" and "I don't like," using gestures, as you model sentences such as, "I like oranges." Have students color, cut out, and then glue the pictures below the correct heading. For younger students, you may wish to draw simple icons of a smile and a frown beside the respective headings to help them complete the page. Review by asking students to tell you which foods they like and which foods they don't like.

EXTENSIONS: Have students draw or cut out from magazines pictures of their favorite foods, including drinks, meats, snacks, etc. Label a piece of construction paper "My Favorite Foods" and provide students with glue to make a collage. When students have finished, ask them questions such as, "What is your favorite drink (snack, fruit, meat, etc.)?" Help students to learn any new vocabulary not included on the food flash cards (pages 140–145).

Have students draw a picture of their favorite meal from their home culture. Ask a bilingual parent volunteer or cross-grade tutor to help them label the food items in the picture. Encourage newcomers to share their drawings with the rest of the class.

K-2 Newcomer Program

OBJECTIVE: To sort illustrated food and drink words into categories

INSTRUCTIONS: Review the vocabulary on the page with students. Use mime, gestures, or pictures to demonstrate the meaning of "Hungry" and "Thirsty." Have students color, cut out, and then glue the pictures below the correct heading. Review by calling out a food or drink and having students respond with "Hungry" or "Thirsty."

EXTENSIONS: Write the headings "Hungry" and "Thirsty" at the top of a piece of construction paper. Have students dictate the names of other things they like to eat or drink when they are hungry and thirsty, either in English or in their home language, to you or to a bilingual cross-grade tutor or parent volunteer. Suggest that they then illustrate the two lists with pictures they draw or cut out from magazines. Encourage students to include items not found on the food flash cards (pages 140–145). Help students to label pictures. Have the bilingual tutor or volunteer translate any home-language words. Help second graders write a sentence for some of the pictures by providing them with a model such as, "I like to drink _____ ."

Make another set of photocopies of the food flash cards (pages 140–145) and have students cut out the foods and sort them into groups of vegetables, meats, fruits, etc. Younger students will be able to do some basic sorting. You might challenge second graders to make a pictorial food chart or pyramid.

OBJECTIVE: To categorize animals by habitat

INSTRUCTIONS: Review the vocabulary on the page by having students point to the appropriate pictures as you call out the animal names. Read aloud the directions, calling students' attention to the crayons. Demonstrate the meaning of "in a tree" and "on the ground," using gestures, mime, or pictures. Before students color the pictures, have them indicate to you, a cross-grade tutor, or a bilingual parent volunteer which of the animals live in a tree and which ones live on the ground.

EXTENSIONS: Have students draw a picture of two animals from their home culture: one that lives in a tree and one that lives on the ground.

Make another set of photocopies of the Animal Dictionary (pages 159–162) and help students cut out all the animals. Have students sort the animals into groups: farm and zoo animals, birds and insects, feathers and fur, etc. Second graders may be ready to classify animals as vertebrates and invertebrates. (Keep in mind that what is considered to be a farm animal in the United States is not necessarily a farm animal in the newcomers' home cultures.)

OBJECTIVES: To follow written and spoken directions that use animal vocabulary, color words, and place prepositions ◆ To write about a picture

INSTRUCTIONS: Look at the picture on page 172 with students. Introduce the vocabulary *tree, grass, log, water, rock,* and *branch* by pointing to the items in the picture and having students repeat the words after you. If necessary, review place prepositions. Read the sentences on page 173 with students. Ask beginning readers to identify the animal words in each sentence. Highlight the animal names with a marker. Have students draw the animals in the correct places and then color them as directed in the instruction lines.

Before children write in Part B, encourage them to describe the picture. Help beginning writers put their ideas on paper. Accept invented spellings and home-language words. Have preliterate students dictate sentences to you. For younger students, you may have to suggest and write some sentences. In both cases, leave out the animal word and allow newcomers the opportunity to write it themselves. Read the sentences aloud for nonreaders.

ESL Student Activity Chart

Name _____

Date _____

	Monday	Tuesday	Wednesday	Thursday	Friday
Listening					
Computer					
ESL Learning Center					
Activity Pages					
Group Work					

Week of _____

K–2 Newcomer Program • Prentice Hall Regents   © by Judie Haynes

See instructions on page T13.

2

Name _____

Date _____

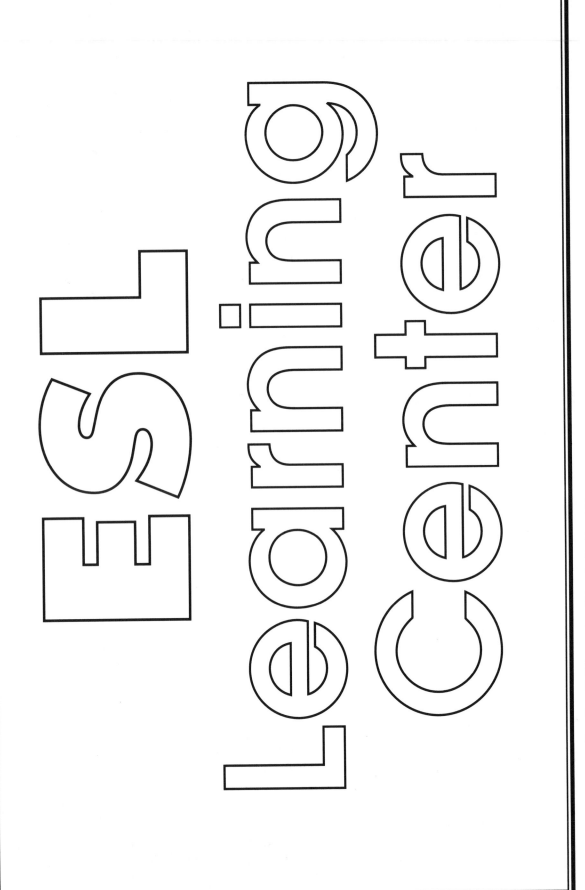

ESL Learning Center

K-2 Newcomer Program • Prentice Hall Regents   © by Judie Haynes

See instructions on page T13.

Classroom Labels—1

door

desk

K-2 Newcomer Program • Prentice Hall Regents © by Judie Haynes

See instructions on page T13.

Classroom Labels—2

chalkboard

chair

K-2 Newcomer Program • Prentice Hall Regents   © by Judie Haynes

See instructions on page T13.

Classroom Labels—3

window

clock

K–2 Newcomer Program • Prentice Hall Regents   © by Judie Haynes

See instructions on page T13.

Classroom Labels—4

map

wastebasket

K–2 Newcomer Program • Prentice Hall Regents   © by Judie Haynes

See instructions on page T13.

Classroom Labels—5

file cabinet

bookshelf

See instructions on page T13.

Classroom Labels—6

✂

flag

closet

K–2 Newcomer Program • Prentice Hall Regents   © by Judie Haynes

See instructions on page T13.

Classroom Directions

color

cut

circle

draw

match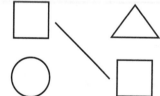

glue

write

See instructions on page T13.

Name _____ Date _____

Color Chart

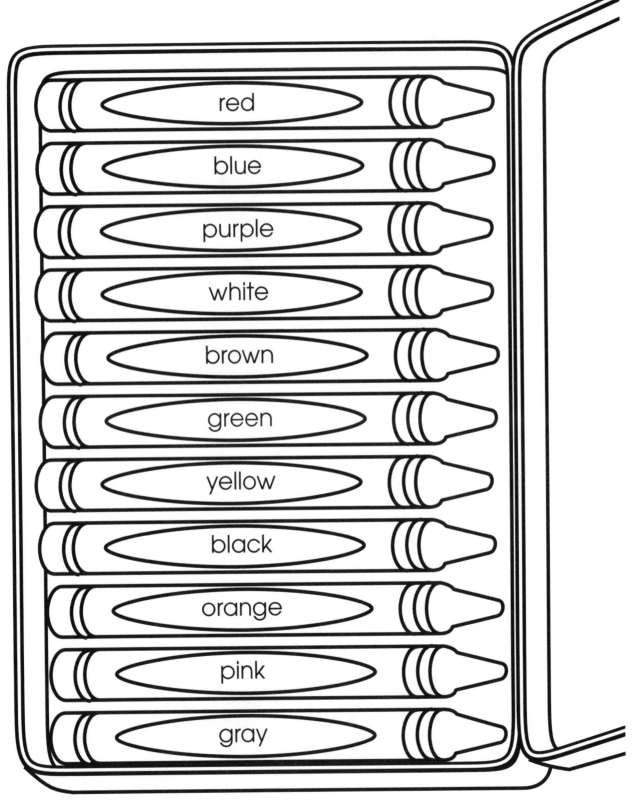

red

blue

purple

white

brown

green

yellow

black

orange

pink

gray

K-2 Newcomer Program • Prentice Hall Regents   © by Judie Haynes

See instructions on page T14.

Colors, Colors Everywhere

Color the cans of paint.

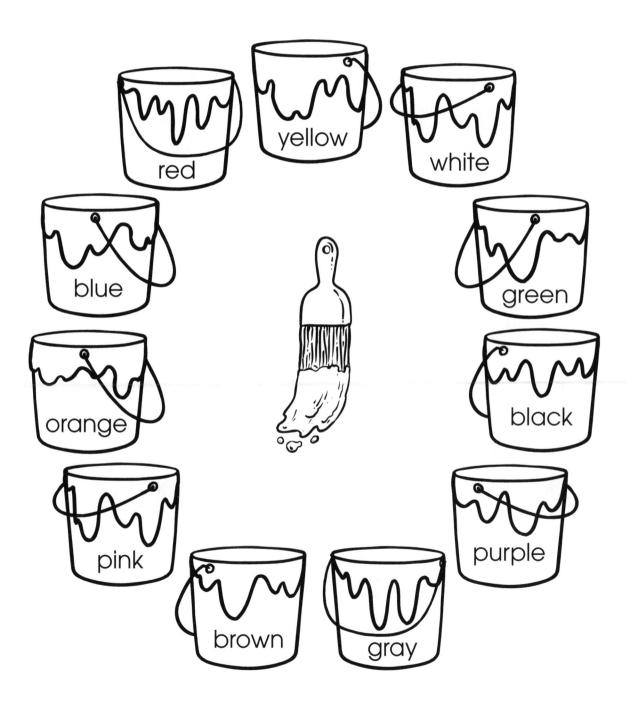

See instructions on page T14.

Name _____ Date _____

Color the Balloons

Color the balloons.

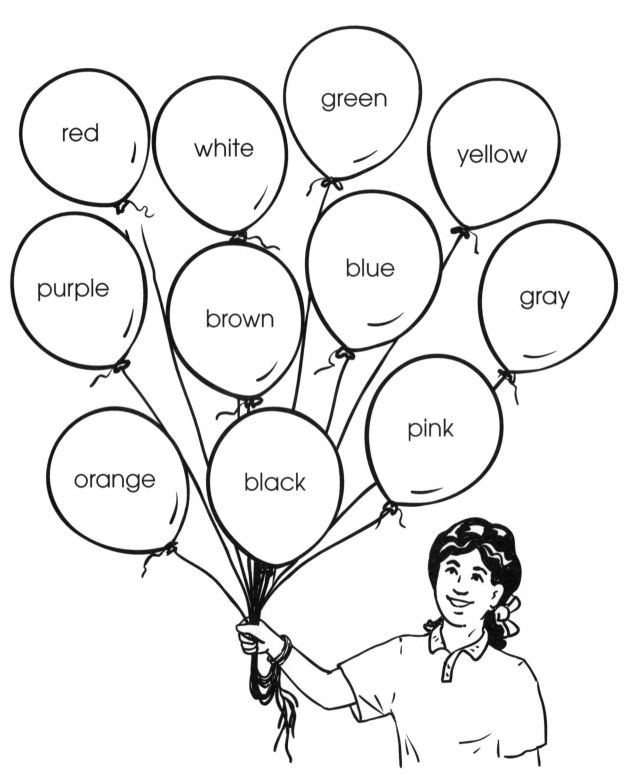

red

white

green

yellow

purple

brown

blue

gray

orange

black

pink

K–2 Newcomer Program • Prentice Hall Regents   © by Judie Haynes

See instructions on page T14.

Colorful Flowers

Color the flowers.

yellow

orange

red

purple

pink

yellow

blue

red

blue

white

orange

purple

green

green

green

green

green

green

green

green

brown

black

See instructions on page T14.

Color the Butterfly

Use the numbers to color the butterfly.

1 = orange   2 = red   3 = black

4 = green   5 = yellow   6 = blue

See instructions on page T14.

K-2 Newcomer Program • Prentice Hall Regents · © by Judie Haynes

Draw 2 Yellow Bananas

1. Draw 2 **yellow**	2. Draw 6 **red**
3. Draw 7 **orange**	4. Draw 3 **pink**
5. Draw 4 **blue** 	6. Draw 5 **green**

See instructions on page T14.

Name _____ Date _____

Shape Dictionary

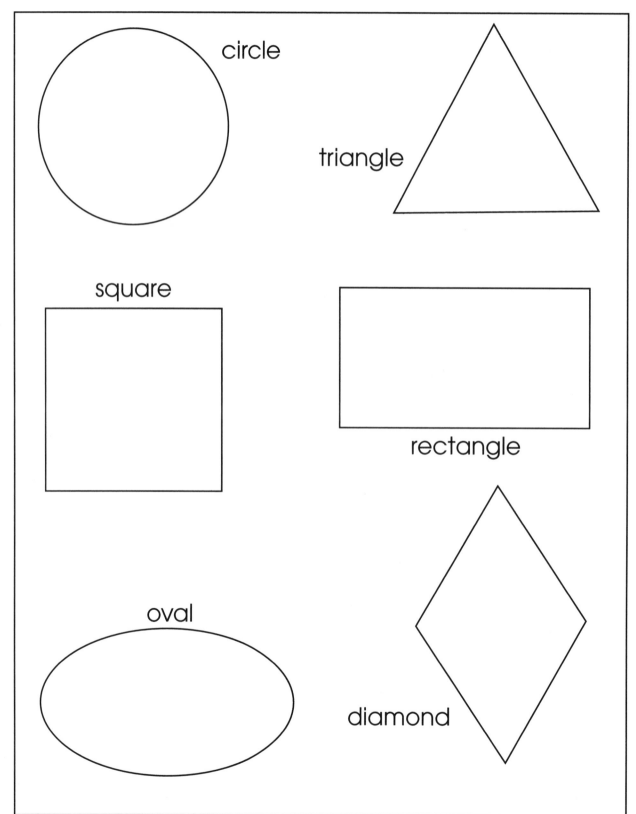

circle

triangle

square

rectangle

oval

diamond

See instructions on pages T14–T15.

K–2 Newcomer Program • Prentice Hall Regents   © by Judie Haynes

Color the Shapes—1

**Outline the squares
with a red crayon.
Color the circles green.**

K-2 Newcomer Program • Prentice Hall Regents © by Judie Haynes

See instructions on page T15.

Name _____ Date _____

Color the Shapes—2

Color the shapes.

brown   black   blue

K-2 Newcomer Program • Prentice Hall Regents   © by Judie Haynes

Color the Shapes—3

1. **Color the squares red.**
2. **Color the rectangles purple.**
3. **Color the circles pink.**
4. **Color the triangles green.**
5. **Color the ovals orange.**
6. **Color the diamond brown.**

See instructions on page T15.

Circle, Rectangle, or Square?—1

Color the pictures.
Cut them out.

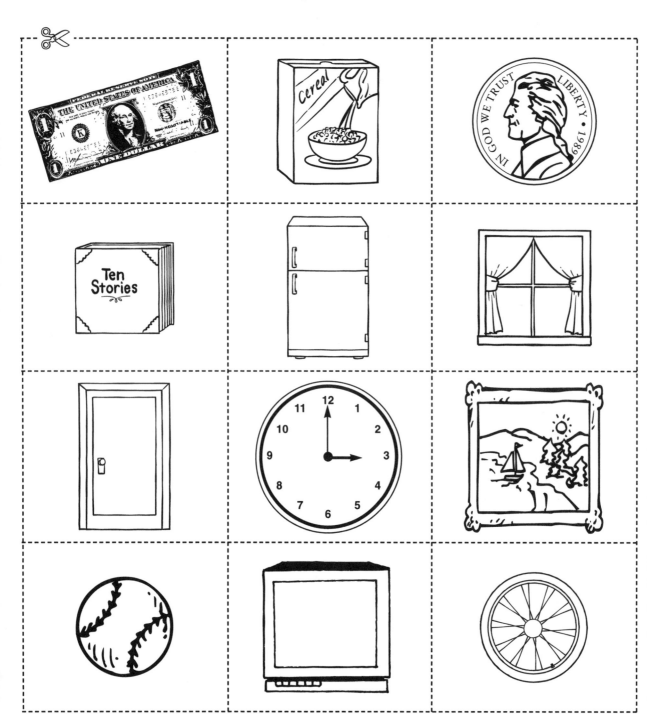

K-2 Newcomer Program • Prentice Hall Regents   © by Judie Haynes

See instructions on page T15.

Circle, Rectangle, or Square?—2

Glue the pictures from page 20 in the correct columns.

Circle	Rectangle	Square

K-2 Newcomer Program • Prentice Hall Regents © by Judie Haynes

See instructions on page T15.

Name _____ Date _____

Number Dictionary

0	zero	
1	one	
2	two	
3	three	
4	four	
5	five	
6	six	
7	seven	
8	eight	
9	nine	
10	ten	
11	eleven	
12	twelve	
13	thirteen	
14	fourteen	
15	fifteen	
16	sixteen	
17	seventeen	
18	eighteen	
19	nineteen	
20	twenty	

K-2 Newcomer Program • Prentice Hall Regents   © by Judie Haynes

See instructions on pages T14–T15.

Circle, Rectangle, or Square?—2

Glue the pictures from page 20 in the correct columns.

Circle	Rectangle	Square

K-2 Newcomer Program • Prentice Hall Regents © by Judie Haynes

See instructions on page T15.

Number Dictionary

0	zero		11	eleven	
1	one		12	twelve	
2	two		13	thirteen	
3	three		14	fourteen	
4	four		15	fifteen	
5	five		16	sixteen	
6	six		17	seventeen	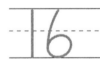
7	seven		18	eighteen	
8	eight		19	nineteen	
9	nine		20	twenty	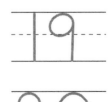
10	ten				

K-2 Newcomer Program • Prentice Hall Regents © by Judie Haynes

See instructions on pages T14–T15.

Match the Numbers—1

**Draw lines to match the numbers and pictures.
Then draw lines to match the pictures and number words.**

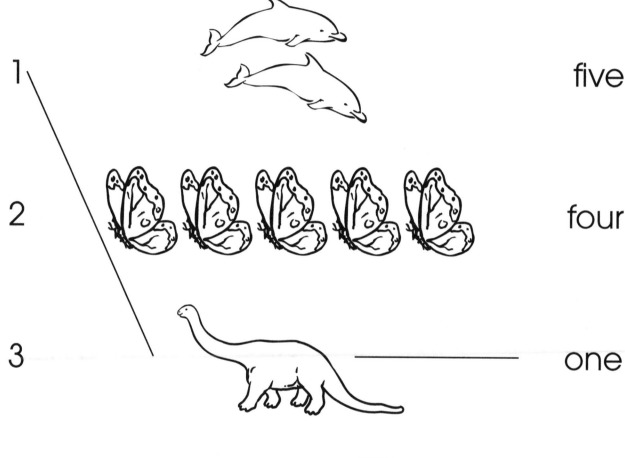

1

2

3 _____

4

5

five

four

one

two

three

K-2 Newcomer Program • Prentice Hall Regents   © by Judie Haynes

See instructions on page T15.

Match the Numbers—2

**Draw lines to match the
numbers and pictures.
Then draw lines to match the
pictures and number words.**

6  nine

7  ten

8  seven

9  eight

10 six

K-2 Newcomer Program • Prentice Hall Regents   © by Judie Haynes

Match the Numbers—3

Draw lines to match the numbers and pictures. Then draw lines to match the pictures and number words.

11 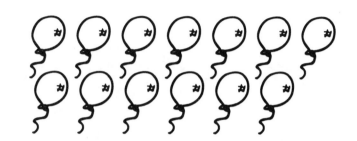 thirteen

12  fifteen

13 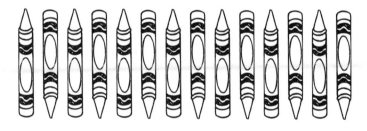 eleven

14  twelve

15  fourteen

See instructions on page T15.

Match the Numbers—4

Draw lines to match the numbers and pictures. Then draw lines to match the pictures and number words.

16

eighteen

17

sixteen

18

twenty

19

seventeen

20

nineteen

K–2 Newcomer Program • Prentice Hall Regents © by Judie Haynes

See instructions on page T15.

Missing Numbers—1

Write the missing numbers.

Copy the numbers from 10–20 in the correct order.

K-2 Newcomer Program • Prentice Hall Regents   © by Judie Haynes

See instructions on page T15.

Name _____   Date _____

Missing Numbers—2

Write the missing numbers.

0	1	2		4	___	6
9	___	11		7	___	9
1	___	3		5	___	7
18	___	20		14	___	16
12	___	14		10	___	12
13	___	15		17	___	19
16	___	18		11	___	13

K-2 Newcomer Program • Prentice Hall Regents   © by Judie Haynes

Find the Fish

Cut out the tails.
Match each tail to the correct fish.

five

three

one

six

two

four

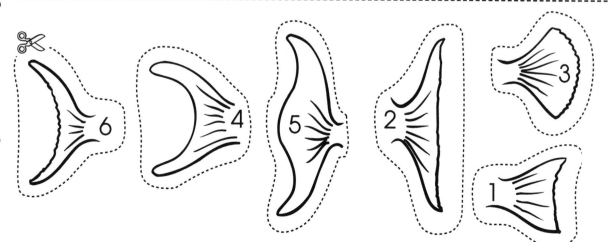

6 4 5 2 3

1

See instructions on page T15.

Name _____ Date _____

Draw Ten Kites

1. Draw **ten** 	2. Draw **four** 
3. Draw **five** 	4. Draw **seven**
5. Draw **nine**	6. Draw **eight**

See instructions on page T16.

K–2 Newcomer Program • Prentice Hall Regents   © by Judie Haynes

Number Words—1

Write the missing number words.

four	sixteen	two	nineteen	five
eleven	eight	fourteen	seventeen	

Zero, one, _____two_____,

three, _____,

_____, six, seven,

_____, nine, ten,

_____, twelve,

thirteen, _____,

fifteen, _____,

_____, eighteen,

_____, twenty.

Name _____ Date _____

Number Words—2

Match the numbers and the number words.

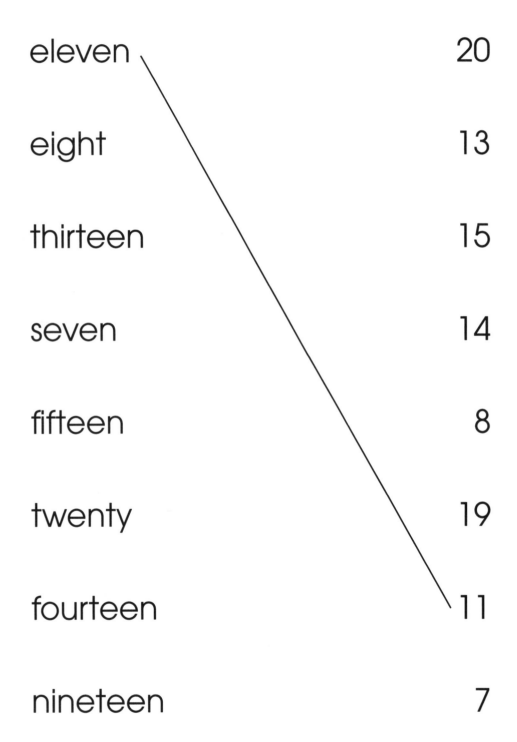

eleven	20
eight	13
thirteen	15
seven	14
fifteen	8
twenty	19
fourteen	11
nineteen	7

K–2 Newcomer Program • Prentice Hall Regents   © by Judie Haynes

The Alphabet—1

Write the letters.

K-2 Newcomer Program • Prentice Hall Regents © by Judie Haynes

See instructions on page T16.

The Alphabet—2

Write the letters.

See instructions on page T16.

K–2 Newcomer Program • Prentice Hall Regents   © by Judie Haynes

The Alphabet—3

Write the letters.

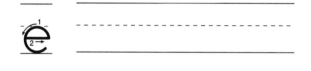

See instructions on page T16.

The Alphabet—4

Write the letters.

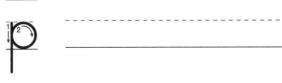

o   ◯ ◯ ◯

p

q

r

s

t

u

v

w

x

y

z

K–2 Newcomer Program • Prentice Hall Regents   © by Judie Haynes

Alphabet Dictionary—1

Color the picture.
Then write the word.

A a apple	B b bird
C c cap	D d duck
E e eraser	F f fish

Match the uppercase and lowercase letters.

E a	D b	C c
A e	B d	F f

See instructions on page T16.

Alphabet Dictionary—2

Color the picture.
Then write the word.

| G g | game | H h | house |

| I i | ice | J j | jacket |

Match the uppercase and lowercase letters.

J	i	A	g
I	f	H	a
F	j	G	h

K-2 Newcomer Program • Prentice Hall Regents   © by Judie Haynes

Alphabet Dictionary—3

Color the picture.
Then write the word.

K k	king	L l	lettuce
M m	monkey	N n	nest
O o	octopus	P p	pencil

Match the uppercase and lowercase letters.

M	n	P	b	O	c
N	m	K	k	C	o
H	h	B	p	L	l

See instructions on page T16.

Alphabet Dictionary—4

Color the picture.
Then write the word.

| Q q   queen | R r   ring | S s   seal |
| T t   tiger | U u   umbrella | |

Match the uppercase and lowercase letters.

Q u	R r	T k
U q	S f	H t
P p	F s	K h

K–2 Newcomer Program • Prentice Hall Regents   © by Judie Haynes

Alphabet Dictionary—5

Color the picture.
Then write the word.

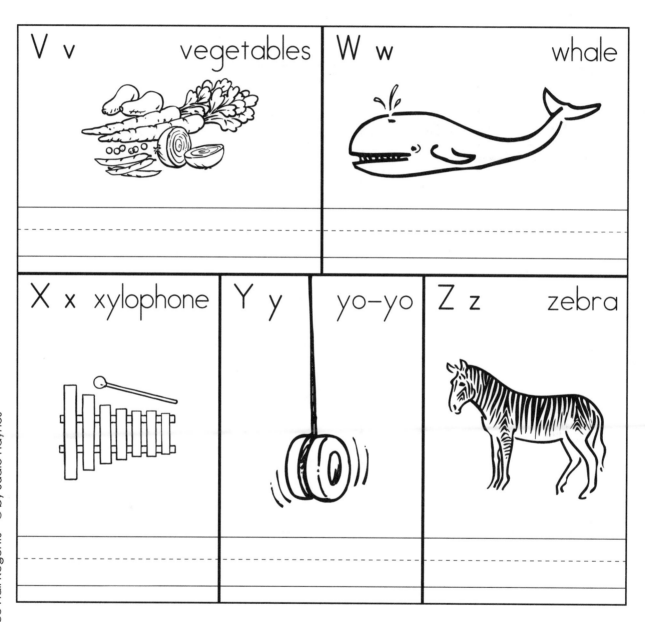

| V v | vegetables | W w | whale |

| X x xylophone | Y y | yo-yo | Z z | zebra |

Match the uppercase and lowercase letters.

M		y	X		y	Z		s
W		m	Y		v	S		z
Y		w	V		x	A		a

K-2 Newcomer Program • Prentice Hall Regents   © by Judie Haynes

See instructions on page T16.

42

Letters, Letters—1

**Circle the first letter in each row.
Then circle the letters that are
the same.**

1.	(F)	E	(F)	T	(F)
2.	P	P	R	D	P
3.	Y	Y	X	Y	Z
4.	G	C	G	G	Q
5.	W	N	W	M	W
6.	K	K	F	T	K
7.	M	N	M	W	M
8.	N	M	N	N	W

See instructions on page T17.

K–2 Newcomer Program • Prentice Hall Regents   © by Judie Haynes

Letters, Letters—2

Circle the first letter in each row. Then circle the letters that are the same.

1.	(b)	(b)	p	q	(b)
2.	w	m	w	v	w
3.	p	b	p	q	p
4.	i	j	i	l	i
5.	n	n	m	h	n
6.	d	b	p	d	d
7.	m	w	n	m	m
8.	g	q	g	j	g

K-2 Newcomer Program • Prentice Hall Regents © by Judie Haynes

See instructions on page T17.

Name _____   Date _____

Find the Engine

Cut out the train cars.
Glue them to the correct engine.

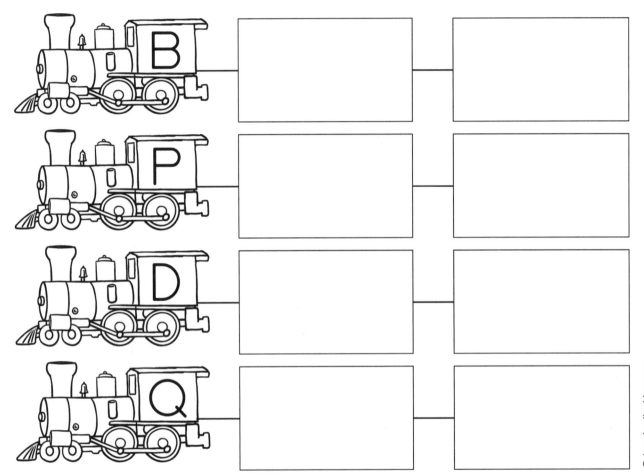

© by Judie Haynes

See instructions on page T17.

Alphabet Match

Match the uppercase and lowercase letters.

J	g	D	b
H	c	B	q
C	j	P	d
G	h	Q	p
E	l	M	n
F	e	W	v
L	i	V	m
I	f	N	w

K-2 Newcomer Program • Prentice Hall Regents © by Judie Haynes

See instructions on page T17.

Name _____ Date _____

Write the Missing Letters

Write the missing letters.

a b c d e f g h i j k l m
n o p q r s t u v w x y z

a b c d _ f _

h _ j _ m

o _ q _ s _

v _ x _ z

Write the letter that comes before.

d e	_ s	_ u
_ c	_ m	_ g
_ p	_ w	_ z

See instructions on page T17.

K-2 Newcomer Program • Prentice Hall Regents   © by Judie Haynes

ABC Order

Put the letters in ABC order.

a b c d e f g h i j k l m
n o p q r s t u v w x y z

j h i g   g   h   i   j

r o q p

c e b d

y v w x

u r s t

f i h g

m k l j

p o m n

K-2 Newcomer Program • Prentice Hall Regents © by Judie Haynes

See instructions on page T17.

Name _____

Date _____

What Is the Date?

Fill in the calendar for this month.

Sunday	Monday	Tuesday	Wednesday	Thursday	Friday	Saturday

See instructions on page T18.

K–2 Newcomer Program • Prentice Hall Regents   © by Judie Haynes

Days of the Week

Write the days of the week in order.

Tuesday   Saturday   Monday   Friday
Wednesday   Sunday   Thursday

1. Sunday

2. M

3. T

4. W

5. T

6. F

7. S

See instructions on page T18.

Name _____ Date _____

Months of the Year
Dictionary—1

January

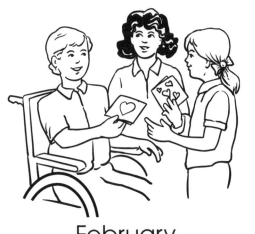

February

March

April

May

June

See instructions on pages T14–T15.

K–2 Newcomer Program • Prentice Hall Regents   © by Judie Haynes

Months of the Year
Dictionary—2

July

August

September

October

November

December

See instructions on pages T14–T15.

Name _____ Date _____

Which Month Is Next?

Write the months in the correct order.

1. January

2. _____

3. _____

4. _____

5. _____

6. _____

7. _____

8. _____

9. _____

10. _____

11. _____

12. _____

September

July

August

March

February

November

December

October

January

May

April

June

K-2 Newcomer Program • Prentice Hall Regents   © by Judie Haynes

How to Make a Snowman—1

Color the pictures.
Cut them out.

K–2 Newcomer Program • Prentice Hall Regents   © by Judie Haynes

See instructions on page T18.

Name _____ Date _____

How to Make a Snowman—2

Put the pictures from page 53 in order.
Glue them in the correct place.

1	2
3	4
5	6

See instructions on page T18.

K–2 Newcomer Program • Prentice Hall Regents   © by Judie Haynes

What Comes Next?—1

Color the pictures.
Then cut them out.

See instructions on page T19.

What Comes Next?—2

Put the pictures from page 55 in order.
Glue them in the correct place.
Use the Months of the Year Dictionary
to help you.

1	2
3	**4**
5	**6**

Name _____ Date _____ 57

Days and Months Word Search

Find each word in the puzzle.
Circle it.

Monday   Saturday   April   September
Tuesday   Sunday   May   October
Wednesday   January   June   November
Thursday   February   July   December
Friday   March   ~~August~~

```
M  A  S  C  A  U  G  U  S  T  J  P
M  S  A  T  U  R  D  A  Y  U  A  J
A  M  O  N  D  A  Y  Y  E  E  N  U
Y  A  C  A  B  P  R  U  S  S  U  L
P  R  T  C  R  R  S  U  N  D  A  Y
U  C  O  F  N  I  O  F  O  A  R  T
N  H  B  M  N  L  V  B  V  Y  Y  H
E  S  E  P  T  E  M  B  E  R  R  U
J  N  R  J  D  E  C  E  M  B  E  R
F  E  B  R  U  A  R  Y  B  A  A  S
L  B  L  R  A  N  R  F  E  E  Y  D
F  R  I  D  A  Y  E  F  R  R  Y  A
N  W  I  W  E  D  N  E  S  D  A  Y
```

K-2 Newcomer Program • Prentice Hall Regents   © by Judie Haynes

See instructions on page T19.

Where Is the Cat?—1
(Dictionary)

in
The cat is **in** the bag.

under
The cat is **under** the bag.

on
The cat is **on** the bag.

next to
The cat is **next to** the bag.

K–2 Newcomer Program • Prentice Hall Regents © by Judie Haynes

Where Is the Cat?—2
(Dictionary)

over
The cat is **over** the bag.

in front of
The cat is **in front of** the bag.

behind
The cat is **behind** the bag.

between
The cat is **between** the bags.

See instructions on page T19.

Name _____ Date _____

Where Is the Dog?

Color the dogs and the boxes.
Cut out the dogs.
Glue them in the correct place.

The dog is **on** the box.

The dog is **between** the boxes.

The dog is **in front of** the box.

The dog is **next to** the box.

See instructions on page T19.

K-2 Newcomer Program • Prentice Hall Regents © by Judie Haynes

Where Is the Bird?

**Color the birds and the nests.
Cut out the birds.
Glue them in the correct place.**

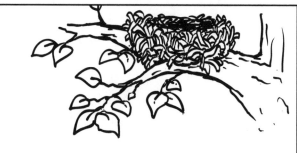

The bird is **under** the nest.

The bird is **over** the nest.

The bird is **in** the nest.

The bird is **behind** the nest.

See instructions on page T19.

Name _____   Date _____

Where Is the Snake?

Color the snakes and the rocks.
Cut out the snakes.
Glue them in the correct place.

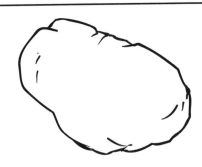

The snake is **under** the rock.

The snake is **on** the rock.

The snake is **between** the rocks.

The snake is **behind** the rock.

See instructions on page T19.

K–2 Newcomer Program • Prentice Hall Regents   © by Judie Haynes

Where Is the Bee?

Color the bees and the beehives.
Cut out the bees.
Glue them in the correct place.

The bee is **over** the hive.

The bee is **next to** the hive.

The bee is **in** the hive.

The bee is **in front of** the hive.

See instructions on page T19.

Name _____ Date _____

Where Are They?—1

Match the animals that are in the same position.

The bee is **under** the hive.

The bird is **over** the nest.

The cat is **over** the bag.

The dog is **behind** the bag.

The dog is **next to** the bag.

The cat is **under** the bag.

The bird is **behind** the nest.

The snake is **next to** the rock.

See instructions on page T20.

Where Are They?—2

Match the animals that are in the same position.

The bee is **on** the hive.

The bird is **in** the nest.

The cat is **in** the bag.

The dog is **between** the bags.

The dog is **in front of** the box.

The cat is **on** the bag.

The bird is **between** the nests.

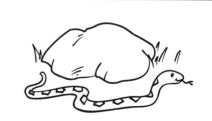

The snake is **in front of** the rock.

See instructions on page T20.

Classroom Flash Card Pictures—1

Color the pictures. Cut them out.
Glue them on cards.

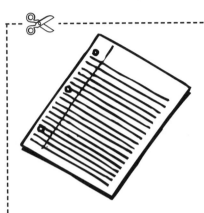  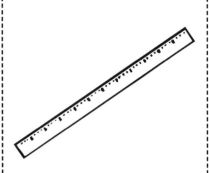

 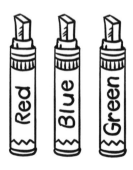 

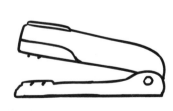  

See instructions on page T20.

K–2 Newcomer Program • Prentice Hall Regents   © by Judie Haynes

Classroom Flash Card Words—1

Glue each word on the back of the correct picture card.

paper	notebook	ruler
book	scissors	glue
crayons	markers	pencil
stapler	eraser	calendar

K–2 Newcomer Program • Prentice Hall Regents © by Judie Haynes

See instructions on page T20.

Classroom Flash Card Pictures—2

Color the pictures. Cut them out.
Glue them on cards.

I like English.

756

NORTH
AMERICA

12 11 10 9 8 7 6 5 4 3 2 1

K-2 Newcomer Program • Prentice Hall Regents　© by Judie Haynes

Classroom Flash Card Words—2

Glue each word on the back of the correct picture card.

✂

computer	chalkboard	bookshelf
flag	window	wastebasket
door	map	pencil sharpener
desk	clock	closet

K-2 Newcomer Program • Prentice Hall Regents © by Judie Haynes

See instructions on page T20.

Name _____ Date _____

Draw a Blue Book

Draw each classroom object.
Copy the name of the object on the line.
Color each picture the correct color.

1. blue **book**	2. yellow **paper**
book	
3. gray **stapler**	4. orange **glue**
5. green **scissors**	6. brown **wastebasket**

See instructions on page T20.

K–2 Newcomer Program • Prentice Hall Regents © by Judie Haynes

Draw a Red Pencil

Draw each classroom object.
Copy the name of the object on the line.
Color each picture the correct color.

1. red **pencil**	2. purple **bookshelf**
pencil	
3. black **notebook**	4. pink **eraser**
5. white **clock**	6. green **markers**

See instructions on page T20.

What Is It?

Connect the dots. Start with *one*.

one	four	seven	ten
two	five	eight	eleven
three	six	nine	twelve

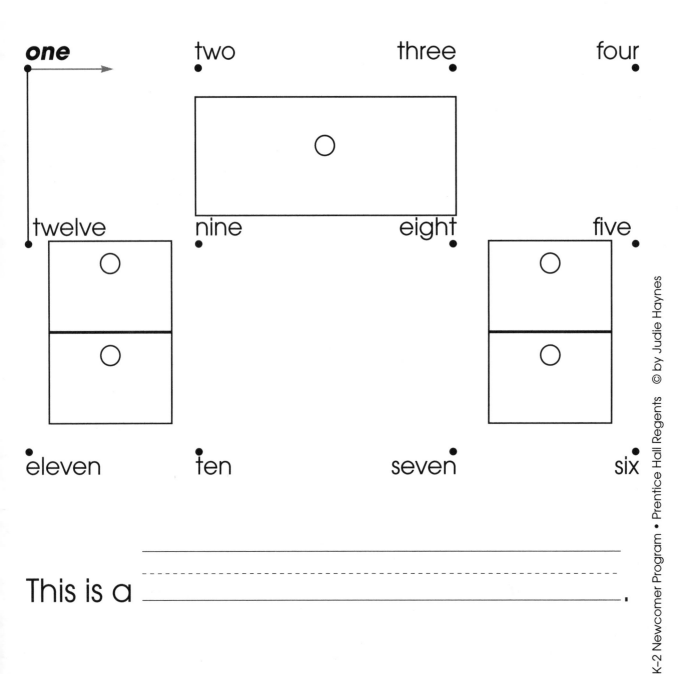

This is a _____.

K–2 Newcomer Program • Prentice Hall Regents   © by Judie Haynes

See instructions on page T20.

Classroom Word Search

Find each word in the puzzle. Circle it.

clock   closet   flag   bookshelf
calendar   stapler   door   chalkboard
window   map   desk   wastebasket
computer   glue   pencil   scissors

C S C B I O R R S W A E F G
L A L G B C S C I S S O R S
O B O O K S H E L F H D I J
C S S L K O G L U E C P H I
K K E C W P I J A P H E A S
J L T H A Q D D W G A N P T
C R B A S L E H W O L C E A
A U C I T L S S I S K I R P
L L D R E G K N N Q B L A L
E E S K B V W N D X O Y S E
N R F L A G M N O A A T E R
D Q K E S S T A W A R M R V
A I Y R K P B P P S D O O R
R J R S E S H A Z R S T T H
L R C O T C O M P U T E R P

See instructions on page T19.

In the Classroom
ABC Order—1

Write the words in ABC order.

a b c d e f g h i j k l m
n o p q r s t u v w x y z

1. 	_____	notebook
2. 	_____	crayons
3.	_____	ruler
4.	_____	eraser
5.	_____	glue
6. 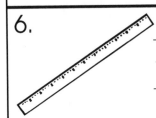	_____	paper

See instructions on page T21.

K-2 Newcomer Program • Prentice Hall Regents   © by Judie Haynes

In the Classroom
ABC Order—2

Write the words in ABC order.

a b c d e f g h i j k l m
n o p q r s t u v w x y z

1. _____ calendar

2. _____ door

3. _____ book

4. _____ scissors

5. _____ map

6. _____ flag

K-2 Newcomer Program • Prentice Hall Regents   © by Judie Haynes

See instructions on page T21.

Name _____ Date _____

One or More?

Cut out each picture.
Glue it in the correct place.

One 	More than one

See instructions on page T21.

In or On?—1

Look at the picture.
Read the sentences on page 78.

See instructions on page T21.

In or On?—2

Look at the picture on page 77.

A. Circle the correct answer.

1. The books are   **in**   **on**   the table.

2. The glue is   **in**   **on**   the desk.

3. The crayons are   **in**   **on**   the chair.

4. The notebook is   **in**   **on**   the desk.

5. The paper is   **in**   **on**   the wastebasket.

6. The clock is   **over**   **under**   the door.

7. The stapler is   **over**   **under**   the chair.

8. The map is   **over**   **under**   the desk.

B. Color the picture on page 77.

1. Color the **table** brown.

2. Color the **desk** brown.

3. Color the **books** green.

4. Color the **crayons** red.

5. Color the **notebook** gray.

6. Color the **glue** orange.

7. Color the **chair** purple.

8. Color the **stapler** black.

9. Color the **map** blue.

10. Color the **clock** yellow.

11. Color the **paper** pink.

12. Color the **wastebasket** green.

K-2 Newcomer Program • Prentice Hall Regents   © by Judie Haynes

See instructions on page T21.

I **have** 2 **names.**

My *American* **given name is**

_____

- ■

1

My *American* **family name is**

_____

- ■

2

In the *United States* **I write my**

name like this.

_____

- -

3

See instructions on page T22.

My NAME PAGE 2

My _____ **given name**
₄

is _____ **.**
₅

My _____ **family name**
₆

is _____ **.**
₇

In _____ **, I write my**
₈

name like this.

9

K–2 Newcomer Program • Prentice Hall Regents   © by Judie Haynes

Places in Your School—1

Find these places in your school.
Write the names of the people.

nurse's office
nurse's
name _____

principal's office
principal's
name _____

main office
secretary's
name _____

water fountain

bathroom

lunchroom

See instructions on page T22.

Places in Your School—2

**Find these places in your school.
Write the teachers' names.**

art room

teacher's
name _____

music room

teacher's
name _____

library

teacher's
name _____

gym

teacher's
name _____

See instructions on page T22.

K-2 Newcomer Program • Prentice Hall Regents   © by Judie Haynes

Parts of the Body Dictionary—1

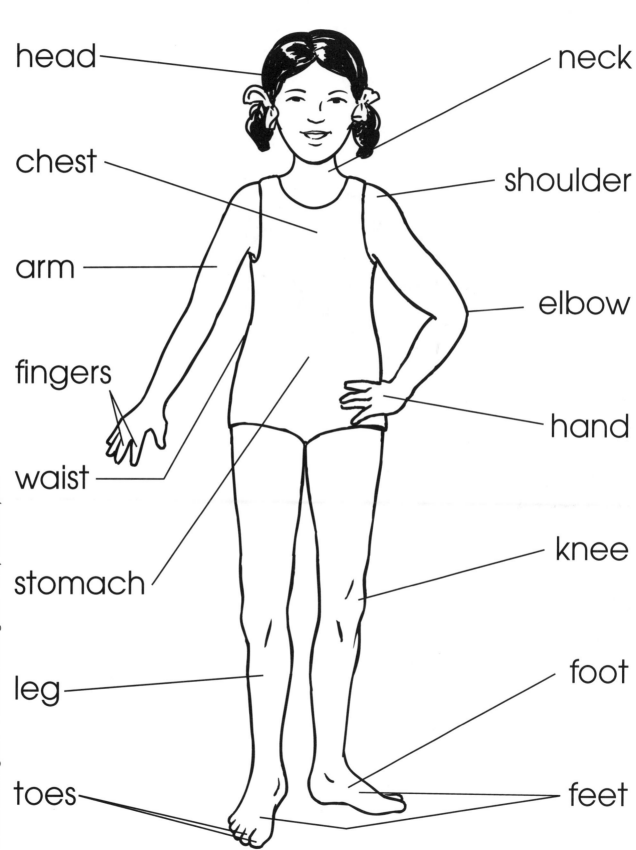

head

chest

arm

fingers

waist

stomach

leg

toes

neck

shoulder

elbow

hand

knee

foot

feet

K-2 Newcomer Program • Prentice Hall Regents   © by Judie Haynes

See instructions on pages T14–T15.

Parts of the Body Dictionary—2
Head

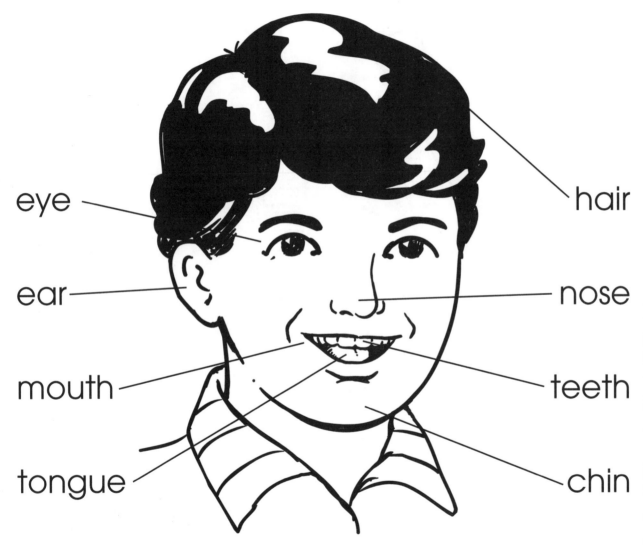

eye

ear

mouth

tongue

hair

nose

teeth

chin

K–2 Newcomer Program • Prentice Hall Regents   © by Judie Haynes

See instructions on pages T14–T15.

Parts of the Body—1

Cut out the words.
Glue each word in the correct place.

hand	stomach	chest	knee
shoulder	arm	foot	leg

See instructions on page T22.

Parts of the Body—2
Head

Cut out the words.
Glue each word in the correct place.

hair	eye	nose	mouth
ear	chin	teeth	tongue

See instructions on page T22.

My Face

Draw a picture of your face.
Use the words to label the picture.

hair   nose   mouth   tongue
eyes   ears   teeth

This is me.

K–2 Newcomer Program • Prentice Hall Regents © by Judie Haynes

See instructions on page T23.

Read, Match, and Write
Body Parts—1

Match each word to the correct picture.
Then write the word.

1. foot

2. neck

3. elbow

 _____ foot

4. leg

5. knee

6. finger

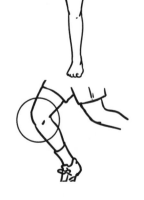

7. arm

K-2 Newcomer Program • Prentice Hall Regents   © by Judie Haynes

See instructions on page T23.

Read, Match, and Write
Body Parts—2

Match each word to the correct picture.
Then write the word.

1. nose

2. ear

3. chin

4. eyes

nose

5. teeth

6. hair

7. mouth

K-2 Newcomer Program • Prentice Hall Regents   © by Judie Haynes

See instructions on page T23.

How Many Toes Do You Have?

Write the correct number on the line.

one   two   ten

1. I have _____ toes.

2. I have _____ head.

3. I have _____ eyes.

4. I have _____ nose.

5. I have _____ chin.

6. I have _____ tongue.

7. I have _____ hands.

8. I have _____ feet.

9. I have _____ fingers.

K–2 Newcomer Program • Prentice Hall Regents   © by Judie Haynes

See instructions on page T23.

Parts of the Body
Word Search

Find each word in the puzzle.
Circle it.

arm	chest	chin	ears	eyes
knee	leg	mouth	nose	shoulder
neck	hand	head	teeth	tongue
hair	fingers	foot	stomach	elbow
waist				

```
J  S  T  E  E  A  R  S  D  Q  B  P  E
N  T  O  F  S  W  A  I  S  T  A  G  Y
E  O  N  A  S  K  S  L  I  E  S  B  U
C  M  G  R  N  P  H  W  S  E  S  K  E
K  A  U  M  N  F  O  O  T  T  H  M  L
S  C  E  X  O  E  Y  E  S  H  O  A  E
F  H  H  G  S  Q  F  H  H  A  U  Y  G
I  V  K  N  E  E  M  I  E  H  L  E  Q
N  Q  I  Z  C  X  O  S  A  A  D  L  U
G  Y  Q  C  H  T  U  Z  D  N  E  B  C
E  N  T  H  E  W  T  J  Q  D  R  O  U
R  U  B  I  S  Z  H  X  A  C  R  W  H
S  Y  T  N  T  Z  E  H  A  I  R  T  O
```

See instructions on page T19.

Name _____ Date _____

A Make-Believe Monster—1

1. Color the monster's  purple.

2. Color the monster's  blue.

3. Color the monster's  green.

4. Color the monster's  orange.

5. Color the monster's  red.

6. Color the monster's  brown.

7. Color the monster's yellow.

8. Color the monster's black.

See instructions on page T23.

K–2 Newcomer Program • Prentice Hall Regents © by Judie Haynes

A Make-Believe Monster—2

Circle the body parts that the monster has.
Put an **X** on what it doesn't have.

Does the monster have . . . ?

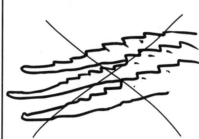 two feet?	three tails?	 two noses?
 three eyes?	 five teeth?	 one ear?
 four legs?	 five hands?	 one head?

See instructions on page T23.

Action Word Dictionary—1

Look at the pictures. Read the words.
Write the words in your ESL notebook.

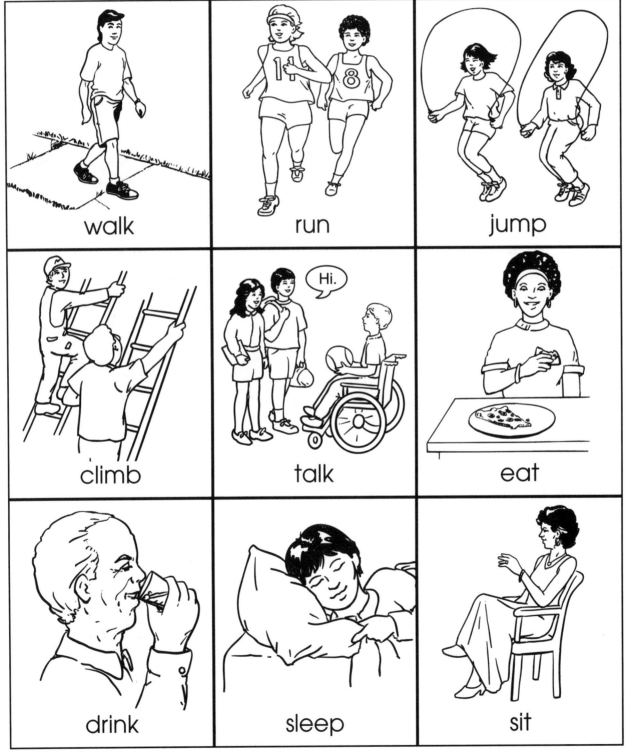

walk run jump

climb talk eat

drink sleep sit

See instructions on pages T14–T15.

K–2 Newcomer Program • Prentice Hall Regents   © by Judie Haynes

Action Word Dictionary—2

Look at the pictures. Read the words.
Write the words in your ESL notebook.

play

read

write

stand

look

listen

point

sing

open

See instructions on pages T14–T15.

Write the Missing Letters—1

Write the missing letters.
Use your Action Word Dictionary
to help you.

listen

sl_e_

po_t

st_d

_lim

d_nk

See instructions on page T24.

K–2 Newcomer Program • Prentice Hall Regents   © by Judie Haynes

Write the Missing Letters—2

**Write the missing letters.
Use your Action Word Dictionary
to help you.**

See instructions on page T24.

Read, Match, and Write
Action Words—1

Match each word to the correct picture.
Then write the word.

1. read

2. drink

3. sleep

4. play   read

5. walk

6. jump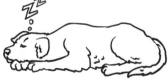

K–2 Newcomer Program • Prentice Hall Regents   © by Judie Haynes

See instructions on page T23.

Read, Match, and Write
Action Words—2

Match each word to the correct picture.
Then write the word.

1. eat

2. run

3. write

eat

4. sing

5. open

6. climb

See instructions on page T23.

Name _____ Date _____

What Can You Do?

Fill in the missing words.

read	listen	write
sit	point	open

1. I can O_____ the door.

2. I can W_____ my name.

3. I can p_____ to the clock.

4. I can l_____ to the teacher.

5. I can S_____ at my desk.

6. I can r_____ a book.

Action or Thing?—1

These are actions.
Actions are what you can do.

read stand listen look

These are things.
Things are what you can touch.

wastebasket pencil table pencil sharpener

Circle the actions.
Underline the things.

  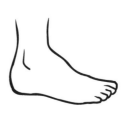 

eat fish foot walk

See instructions on page T24.

Action or Thing?—2

Cut out the pictures.
Glue each in the correct place.

Action	Thing

write

point

legs

ruler

open

clock

sleep

picture

K-2 Newcomer Program • Prentice Hall Regents   © by Judie Haynes

Clothing Dictionary—1

Color the pictures.
Read the words.
Write them in your ESL notebook.

dress   skirt   jeans

sweater   suit   jacket

shorts   sweatshirt   shirt

K-2 Newcomer Program • Prentice Hall Regents © by Judie Haynes

See instructions on pages T14–T15.

Name _____ Date _____

Clothing Dictionary—2

Color the pictures.
Read the words.
Write them in your ESL notebook.

purse

backpack

cap

socks

sneakers

blouse

tie

shoes

belt

earrings

necklace

ring

See instructions on pages T14–T15.

K-2 Newcomer Program • Prentice Hall Regents   © by Judie Haynes

Clothing Dictionary—3

Color the pictures.
Read the words.
Write them in your ESL notebook.

mittens

raincoat

pajamas

scarf

bathing suit

T-shirt

sandals

sundress

boots

bathrobe

umbrella

sunglasses

See instructions on pages T14–T15.

K–2 Newcomer Program • Prentice Hall Regents   © by Judie Haynes

Draw a Red Umbrella

Draw each article of clothing.
Copy the clothing word on the line.
Color each picture.

1. red **umbrella**	2. gray **sweater**
umbrella	
3. black **jacket**	4. blue **blouse**
5. yellow **shirt**	6. green **tie**

See instructions on page T20.

K–2 Newcomer Program • Prentice Hall Regents   © by Judie Haynes

Draw Orange Mittens

Draw each article of clothing.
Copy the clothing word on the line.
Color each picture.

1. orange **mittens** mittens	2. white **boots**
3. brown **purse**	4. pink **skirt**
5. yellow **dress**	6. purple **pajamas**

K-2 Newcomer Program • Prentice Hall Regents   © by Judie Haynes

See instructions on page T20.

Name _____ Date _____

What Am I Wearing?—1

Connect the dots. Start with *h*.

a b c d e f g h i j k l m
n o p q r s t u v w x y z

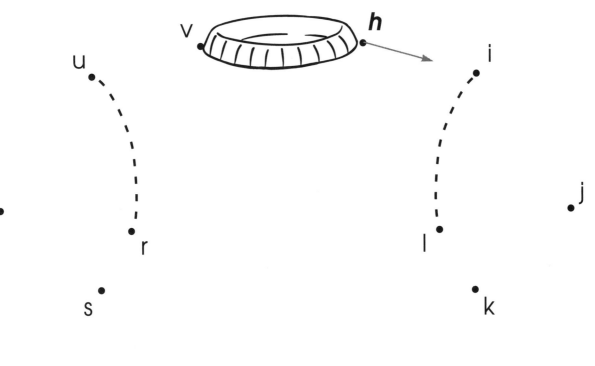

This is a _____.

K–2 Newcomer Program • Prentice Hall Regents   © by Judie Haynes

What Am I Wearing?—2

Connect the dots. Start with a.

a b c d e f g h i j k l m
n o p q r s t u v w x y z

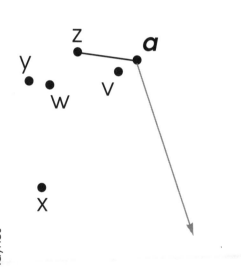

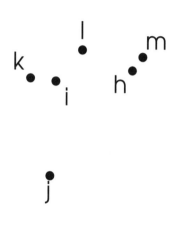

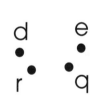

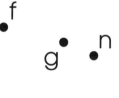

These are _____.

See instructions on page T20.

Name _____ Date _____

What's Different?

Look at each row.
What does not belong there?
Put an X on it.

1
| dress | jeans | pencil | blouse | skirt |

2
| sandals | flag | socks | boots | shoes |

3
| jacket | sweatshirt | shirt | wastebasket | sweater |

4
| chair | bathing suit | sundress | T-shirt | shorts |

See instructions on page T24.

K-2 Newcomer Program • Prentice Hall Regents   © by Judie Haynes

Clothing Word Search

Find each word in the puzzle. Circle it.

dress	suit	jacket	backpack
tie	sweatpants	blouse	jeans
shoes	necklace	sneakers	sweatshirt
shorts	pajamas	skirt	cap
ring	earrings	sandals	mittens
purse	sweater	umbrella	shirt

```
S  S  N  E  S  S  K  I  R  T  G  S
W  S  A  N  D  A  L  S  R  N  S  H
E  E  B  E  R  I  N  G  I  N  W  O
A  J  A  C  K  E  T  R  C  C  E  E
T  O  C  K  S  H  O  R  T  S  A  S
S  O  K  L  L  D  R  E  S  S  T  U
H  C  P  A  J  A  M  A  S  R  P  M
I  A  A  C  E  P  U  R  S  E  A  B
R  P  C  E  A  T  T  R  E  M  N  R
T  K  K  N  N  I  G  I  P  S  T  E
B  L  O  U  S  E  E  N  S  I  S  L
S  W  E  A  T  E  R  G  U  U  M  L
S  N  E  A  K  E  R  S  S  K  I  A
N  W  E  A  M  I  T  T  E  N  S  T
```

K-2 Newcomer Program • Prentice Hall Regents   © by Judie Haynes

See instructions on page T19.

Warm Weather or Cold?—1

Color the pictures.
Cut them out.

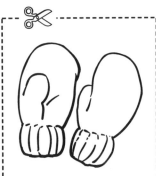

mittens

T-shirt

sandals

sunglasses

jacket

shorts

sweater

boots

bathing suit

scarf

hat

sundress

K–2 Newcomer Program • Prentice Hall Regents   © by Judie Haynes

Warm Weather or Cold?—2

Glue the pictures from page 112 in the correct place.

warm weather	cold weather

See instructions on page T25.

Dressing for a Cold Day—1

Color the pictures.
Cut them out.

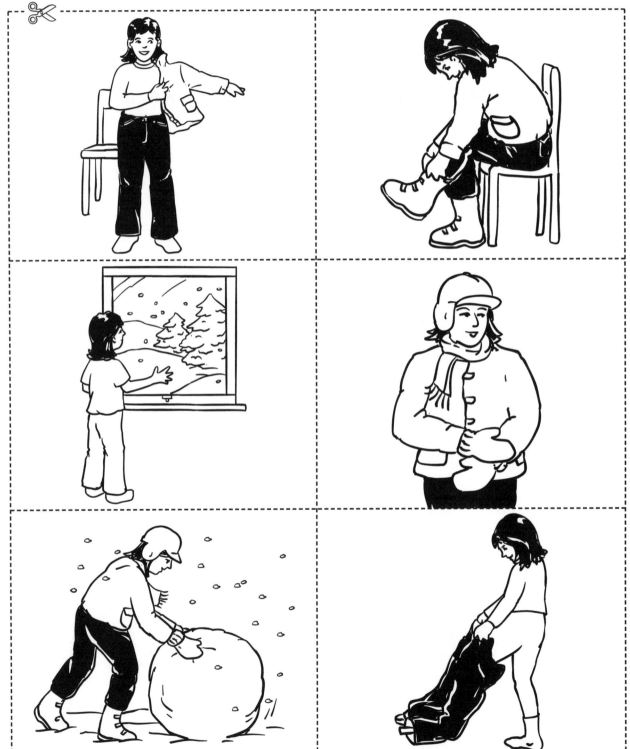

K–2 Newcomer Program • Prentice Hall Regents   © by Judie Haynes

Dressing for a Cold Day—2

Glue the pictures from page 114 in the correct order.

1	2
3	4
5	6

K-2 Newcomer Program • Prentice Hall Regents   © by Judie Haynes

See instructions on page T18.

Clothing ABC Order—1

Write the words in ABC order.

a b c d e f g h i j k l m
n o p q r s t u v w x y z

1.  _____

ring

2.  _____

earrings

3.  _____

blouse

4.  _____

dress

5.  _____

jacket

6. _____

purse

See instructions on page T21.

K-2 Newcomer Program • Prentice Hall Regents © by Judie Haynes

Clothing ABC Order—2

Write the words in ABC order.

a b c d e f g h i j k l m
n o p q r s t u v w x y z

1.  _____

2.  _____

3.  _____

4. 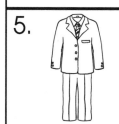 _____

5.  _____

6. _____

suit

socks

shirt

sweater

skirt

sneakers

K-2 Newcomer Program • Prentice Hall Regents © by Judie Haynes

See instructions on page T21.

Name _____ Date _____

Clothing Crossword

Look at the clues.
Fill in the puzzle with clothing words.

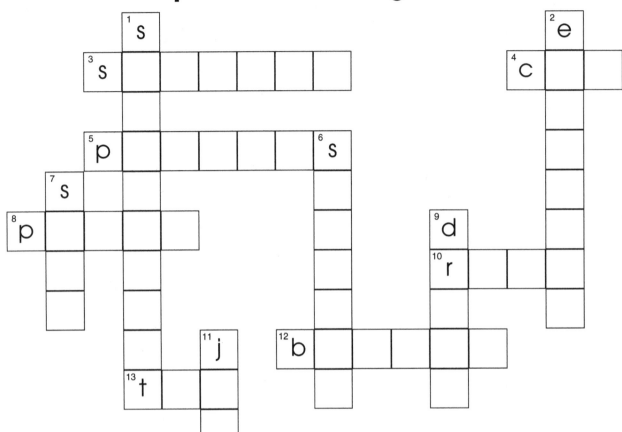

Across

3

4

5

8

10

12

13

Down

1

2

6

7

9

11

See instructions on page T25.

Clothing ABC Order—2

Write the words in ABC order.

a b c d e f g h i j k l m
n o p q r s t u v w x y z

1.		suit
2.		socks
3.		shirt
4.		sweater
5.		skirt
6.		sneakers

See instructions on page T21.

Clothing Crossword

Look at the clues.
Fill in the puzzle with clothing words.

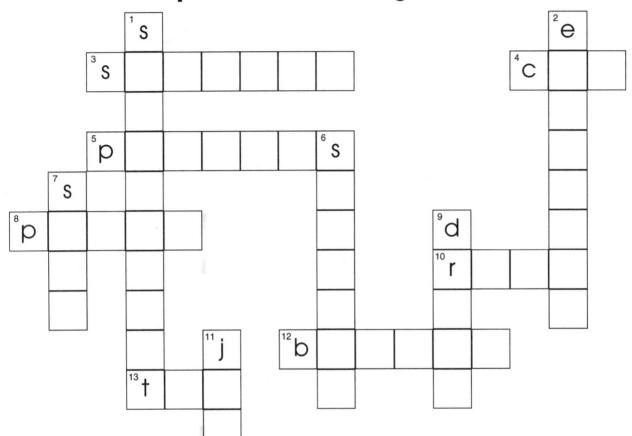

Across

3

4

5

8

10

12

13

Down

1

2

6

7

9

11

See instructions on page T25.

House Dictionary—1

Color the pictures.
Read the words.
Write them in your ESL notebook.

bedroom

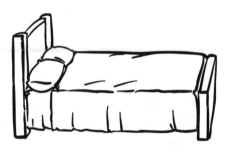

bed

dresser

night table

rug

lamp

toy box

See instructions on pages T14–T15.

Name _____ Date _____

House Dictionary—2

Color the pictures.
Read the words.
Write them in your ESL notebook.

bathroom

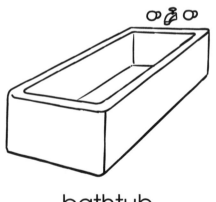

bathtub

mirror

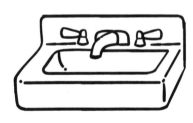

sink

toilet

shower

hamper

See instructions on pages T14–T15.

House Dictionary—3

Color the pictures.
Read the words.
Write them in your ESL notebook.

kitchen

table

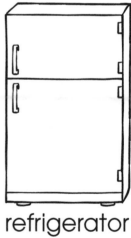

refrigerator

freezer

stove

oven

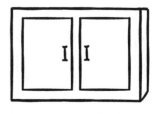

cabinets

See instructions on pages T14–T15.

House Dictionary—4

Color the pictures.
Read the words.
Write them in your ESL notebook.

living room

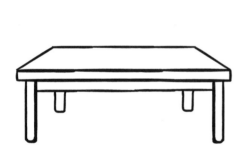

coffee table

sofa

television   floor lamp

armchair

See instructions on pages T14–T15.

K-2 Newcomer Program • Prentice Hall Regents   © by Judie Haynes

Where Does It Go?—1

Color the pictures.
Cut them out.
Glue each picture in the correct
room of the house.

Bathroom	Bedroom

bathtub	bed	dresser	mirror
night table	hamper	sink	lamp

See instructions on page T25.

Where Does It Go?—2

Color the pictures.
Cut them out.
Glue each picture in the correct
room of the house.

Living Room	Kitchen

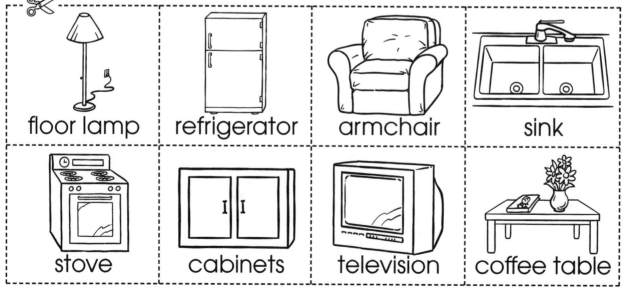

floor lamp	refrigerator	armchair	sink
stove	cabinets	television	coffee table

See instructions on page T25.

Hamper or Desk?—1

Color the pictures.
Cut them out.

scissors	T-shirt	book	sweatpants
crayons	skirt	calendar	blouse
chalk	dress	sweatshirt	notebook

K–2 Newcomer Program • Prentice Hall Regents © by Judie Haynes

See instructions on page T25.

Hamper or Desk?—2

Glue the pictures from page 125 in the correct place.

hamper	desk

K-2 Newcomer Program • Prentice Hall Regents   © by Judie Haynes

Inside or Outside?

Color **objects found inside the house.**

Color **objects found outside the house.**

1. chimney

2. mirror

3. lamp

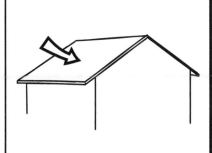

4. roof

5. driveway

6. shower

7. porch

8. dresser

9. toy box

K-2 Newcomer Program • Prentice Hall Regents © by Judie Haynes

See instructions on page T26.

House Word Search

Find each word in the puzzle.
Circle it.

~~bathroom~~	cabinets	mirror	sink
television	hamper	table	shower
refrigerator	dresser	stove	bathtub
lamp	porch	bed	rug
freezer	toilet	oven	sofa

```
Q T S B B A T H R O O M L P
R I M B A T H T U B C L U T
M E T E L E V I S I O N G A
I F F F P R Z T O I L E T B
R B Q R V U F R E E Z E R L
R P C U I G S K U S W T C E
O Z O F S G H T E S O Z N F
R J V R N H E N O R I F G H
Q F G E C D O R M V I N A A
J H V Y Z H L W A B E D K M
K O I S D T Y A E T X L C P
D R E S S E R J M R O A T E
R W V C D B K O U P Q R W R
C C A B I N E T S H A E N S
```

K-2 Newcomer Program • Prentice Hall Regents   © by Judie Haynes

House ABC Order—1

Write the words in ABC order.

a b c d e f g h i j k l m
n o p q r s t u v w x y z

1.		hamper
2.		lamp
3.		television
4.		dresser
5.		bed
6.		sink

K-2 Newcomer Program • Prentice Hall Regents   © by Judie Haynes

See instructions on page T21.

House ABC Order—2

Write the words in ABC order.

a b c d e f g h i j k l m
n o p q r s t u v w x y z

1.  _____

roof

2.  _____

oven

3.  _____

armchair

4.  _____

table

5. 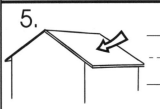 _____

driveway

6.  _____

chimney

K–2 Newcomer Program • Prentice Hall Regents   © by Judie Haynes

House ABC Order—1

Write the words in ABC order.

a b c d e f g h i j k l m
n o p q r s t u v w x y z

1.  _____ hamper

2.  _____ lamp

3.  _____ television

4. 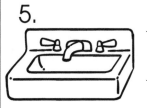 _____ dresser

5.  _____ bed

6. _____ sink

K-2 Newcomer Program • Prentice Hall Regents   © by Judie Haynes

See instructions on page T21.

House ABC Order—2

Write the words in ABC order.

a b c d e f g h i j k l m
n o p q r s t u v w x y z

1. 	_____	roof
2. 	_____	oven
3. 	_____	armchair
4. 	_____	table
5. 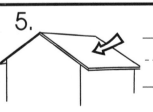	_____	driveway
6. 	_____	chimney

See instructions on page T21.

Toy Dictionary—1

Color the pictures.
Read the words.
Write them in your ESL notebook.

	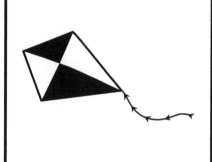	
ball	kite	drum

blocks	doll	teddy bear

roller blades	game	bike

See instructions on pages T14–T15.

Toy Dictionary—2

Color the pictures.
Read the words.
Write them in your ESL notebook.

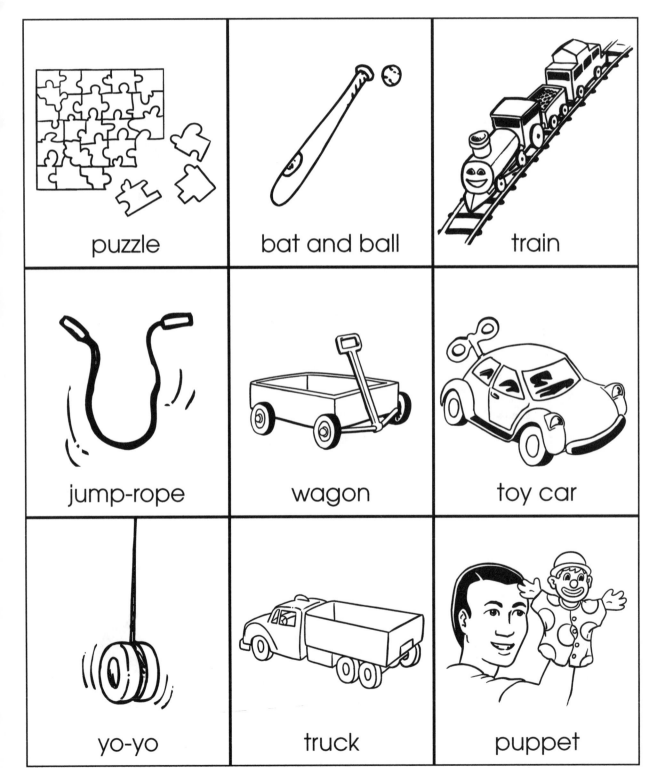

puzzle	bat and ball	train
jump-rope	wagon	toy car
yo-yo	truck	puppet

K–2 Newcomer Program • Prentice Hall Regents   © by Judie Haynes

See instructions on pages T14–T15.

Draw an Orange Kite

Draw each toy.
Copy the name of
the toy on the line.
Color each picture.

1. orange **kite**	2. brown **teddy bear**
kite	
3. green **yo-yo**	4. red **bike**
5. brown **bat**	6. blue **car**

See instructions on page T20.

Draw a Red Wagon

**Draw each toy.
Copy the name of
the toy on the line.
Color each picture.**

1. red **wagon**	2. pink **jump-rope**
wagon	
3. green **ball**	4. gray **roller blades**
5. purple **blocks**	6. orange **puppet**

K–2 Newcomer Program • Prentice Hall Regents   © by Judie Haynes

Draw an Orange Kite

**Draw each toy.
Copy the name of
the toy on the line.
Color each picture.**

1. orange **kite** _kite_	2. brown **teddy bear**
3. green **yo-yo**	4. red **bike**
5. brown **bat**	6. blue **car**

K-2 Newcomer Program • Prentice Hall Regents   © by Judie Haynes

See instructions on page T20.

Name _____   Date _____

Draw a Red Wagon

Draw each toy.
Copy the name of
the toy on the line.
Color each picture.

1. red **wagon**	2. pink **jump-rope**
wagon	
3. green **ball**	4. gray **roller blades**
5. purple **blocks**	6. orange **puppet**

See instructions on page T20.

What Goes Together?

Color all the pictures.
Cut out the bottom row.
Match each picture to its group.
Glue it in place.

jump-rope	bike	teddy bear	
triangle	square	circle	
notebook	paper	ruler	
coffee table	lamp	dresser	

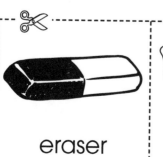

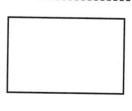

eraser	sofa	wagon	rectangle

See instructions on page T26.

Name _____ Date _____

Toy Box or Desk?—1

Color the pictures.
Cut them out.

 doll	 game	 glue	 eraser
 pencil	 ball	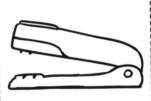 stapler	 puzzle
 roller blades	 paper	 blocks	 markers

K-2 Newcomer Program • Prentice Hall Regents   © by Judie Haynes

See instructions on page T25.

Toy Box or Desk?—2

Glue the pictures from page 136 in the correct place.

toy box	desk

K-2 Newcomer Program • Prentice Hall Regents © by Judie Haynes

See instructions on page T25.

Is the Doll in the Toy Box?—1

Look at the picture.
Answer the questions on page 139.

K–2 Newcomer Program • Prentice Hall Regents   © by Judie Haynes

See instructions on page T26.

Is the Doll in the Toy Box?—2

Look at the picture on page 138.
Circle the correct answers.

1. Is the doll **in** the toy box?   Yes   No

2. Is the cap **on** the bookshelf?   Yes   No

3. Is the toy car **next to** the lamp?   Yes   No

4. Is the picture **over** the dresser?   Yes   No

5. Is the jacket **in** the closet?   Yes   No

6. Is the ball **behind** the dresser?   Yes   No

7. Is the teddy bear **in front of**   Yes   No
   the dresser?

8. Is the shoe **under** the bed?   Yes   No

9. Is the sock **in front of** the bookshelf?   Yes   No

10. Is the train **between** the bed and   Yes   No
    the toy box?

11. Is the cat sleeping **on** the bed?   Yes   No

See instructions on page T26.

Name _____ Date _____

Food Flash Card Pictures—1

**Color the pictures. Cut them out.
Glue them on cards.**

See instructions on page T20.

K–2 Newcomer Program • Prentice Hall Regents   © by Judie Haynes

Food Flash Card Words—1

Glue each word on the back of the correct card.

banana	apple	oranges
grapes	pear	strawberries
carrot	peas	green beans
corn	lettuce	beans

See instructions on page T20.

Food Flash Card Pictures—2

Color the pictures. Cut them out.
Glue them on cards.

See instructions on page T20.

K-2 Newcomer Program • Prentice Hall Regents   © by Judie Haynes

Food Flash Card Words—2

Glue each word on the back of the correct card.

sandwich	fish	potato
chicken	hamburger	eggs
spaghetti	pizza	onion
hot dog	milk	juice

K-2 Newcomer Program • Prentice Hall Regents   © by Judie Haynes

See instructions on page T20.

Food Flash Card Pictures—3

**Color the pictures. Cut them out.
Glue them on cards.**

K–2 Newcomer Program • Prentice Hall Regents   © by Judie Haynes

See instructions on page T20.

Food Flash Card Words—3

Glue each word on the back of the correct card.

water	coffee	tea
rice	soup	salad
bread	french fries	cheese
tomato	popcorn	watermelon

K–2 Newcomer Program • Prentice Hall Regents   © by Judie Haynes

See instructions on page T20.

Draw a Yellow Banana

Draw each food.
Copy the food word on the line.
Color each picture.

1. yellow **banana**	2. green **beans**
banana	
3. red **apple**	4. brown **potatoes**
5. orange **carrots**	6. yellow **corn**

K–2 Newcomer Program • Prentice Hall Regents   © by Judie Haynes

Draw a Blue Fish

Draw each food.
Copy the food word on the line.
Color each picture.

1. blue **fish**	2. red **strawberries**
fish	
3. green **peas**	4. white **eggs**
5. yellow **cheese**	6. purple **grapes**

K-2 Newcomer Program • Prentice Hall Regents   © by Judie Haynes

See instructions on page T20.

Name _____   Date _____

Are You Thirsty?

Connect the dots. Start with *a*.

a b c d e f g h i j k l m
n o p q r s t u v w x y z

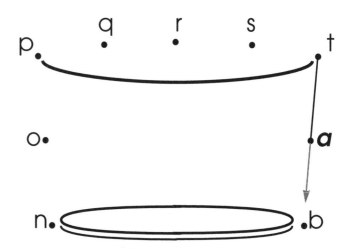

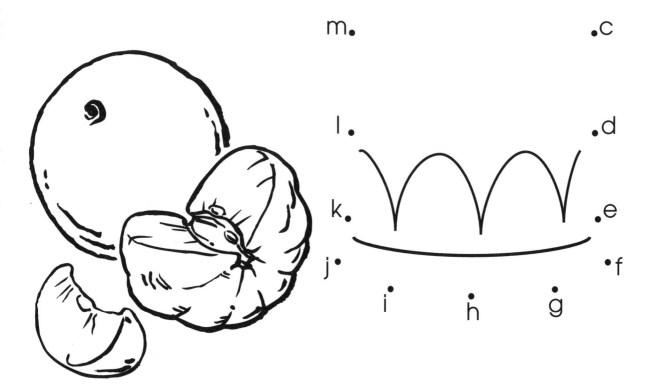

This is orange _____.

See instructions on page T20.

K–2 Newcomer Program • Prentice Hall Regents   © by Judie Haynes

Yum! What Is It?

Connect the dots. Start with *one*.

one	six	eleven	sixteen
two	seven	twelve	seventeen
three	eight	thirteen	eighteen
four	nine	fourteen	nineteen
five	ten	fifteen	

eighteen

seventeen   nineteen

sixteen   **one**

.fifteen   .two

fourteen   thirteen   three.

                        .six   four.

                                                five

twelve

.eleven

                                                        seven

ten   eight

              nine

This is a _____

What Do You Like to Eat?

Color the pictures. Cut them out.
Glue each picture in the correct place.

I like	I don't like

chicken

eggs

hot dogs

green beans

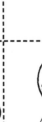

spaghetti

oranges

french fries

cheese

See instructions on page T26.

© by Judie Haynes

K–2 Newcomer Program • Prentice Hall Regents

Hungry or Thirsty?

Color the pictures. Cut them out.
Glue each picture in the correct place.

Hungry	Thirsty

milk

popcorn

sandwich

juice

water · fish · pear

tea

See instructions on page T27.

What Goes Together?—1

Color all the pictures.
Cut out the bottom row.
Match each picture to its group.
Glue it in place.

strawberries	oranges	apple	
carrot	green beans	lettuce	
hot dog	chicken	pizza	
milk	juice	tea	

| corn | pear | water | hamburger |

See instructions on page T26.

What Goes Together?—2

Color all the pictures.
Cut out the bottom row.
Match each picture to its group.
Glue it in place.

armchair	table	sofa	
carrot	lettuce	green beans	
shorts	cap	T-shirt	
bike	doll	bear	

ball	lamp	bathing suit	corn

K-2 Newcomer Program • Prentice Hall Regents © by Judie Haynes

See instructions on page T26.

What Goes Together?—3

Color all the pictures.
Cut out the bottom row.
Match each picture to its group.
Glue it in place.

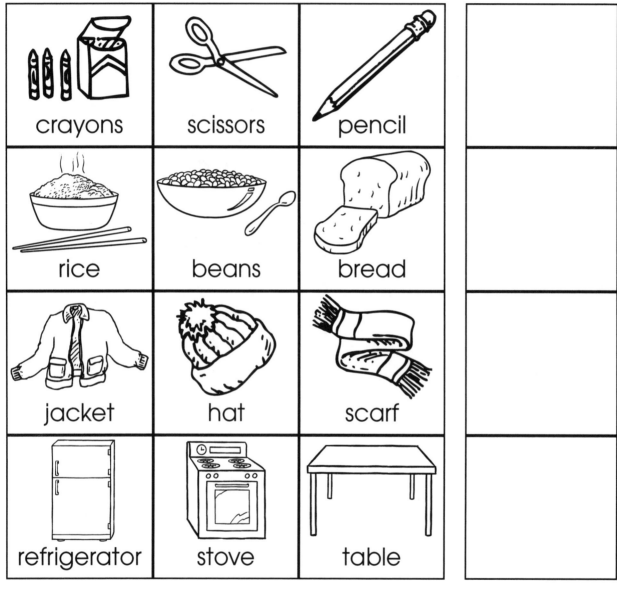

crayons	scissors	pencil	
rice	beans	bread	
jacket	hat	scarf	
refrigerator	stove	table	

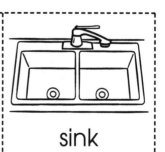

| potato | glue | mittens | sink |

See instructions on page T26.

K-2 Newcomer Program • Prentice Hall Regents　© by Judie Haynes

Closet or Refrigerator?—1

Color the pictures.
Cut them out.

jacket	ice	peas	dress
juice	sneakers	fish	skirt
suit	strawberries	eggs	blouse
salad	milk	shirt	tie

See instructions on page T25.

Closet or Refrigerator?—2

**Glue the pictures from page 155
in the correct place.**

closet	refrigerator

Food Word Search

Find each word in the puzzle.
Circle it.

~~strawberry~~	bread	milk	banana
hamburger	pizza	peas	beans
spaghetti	apple	potato	
soup	corn	pear	
chicken	rice	grapes	

```
N S A P P L E H Z A B Z Q P
X C T A A K C H I C K E N M
S B B R R S K Z T B R B X P
W H B E A N S O Q O H P W O
C V Y H H W R I T V I Y H T
C J M A A R B G R A P E S A
P O D B B M P E V Y L W E T
B E R C R E B I R I C E I O
A J A N N E G U Z R H S V G
N J A S S O A K R Z Y O O H
A Q N H H F L D S G A U P N
N O V T T I F S G Y E P E R
A B O M M H J Y V D A R A A
V H Q S P A G H E T T I R K
```

See instructions on page T19.

Food Crossword

**Look at the clues.
Fill in the puzzle with food words.**

Across

2  9

4  10

8

Down

1  5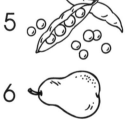

2  6

3  7

8

See instructions on page T25.

Animal Dictionary—1

Color the pictures.
Read the words.
Write them in your ESL notebook.

monkey	elephant	zebra
giraffe	lion	kangaroo
parrot	tiger	hippopotamus

K–2 Newcomer Program • Prentice Hall Regents   © by Judie Haynes

See instructions on pages T14–T15.

Name _____ Date _____

Animal Dictionary—2

Color the pictures.
Read the words.
Write them in your ESL notebook.

cow	horse	sheep
duck	chicken	pig
cat	dog	squirrel

K-2 Newcomer Program • Prentice Hall Regents © by Judie Haynes

See instructions on pages T14–T15.

Animal Dictionary—3

Color the pictures.
Read the words.
Write them in your ESL notebook.

fox	rabbit	snake
mouse	turtle	bear
deer	owl	bird

K–2 Newcomer Program • Prentice Hall Regents   © by Judie Haynes

See instructions on pages T14–T15.

Name _____ Date _____

Animal Dictionary—4

Color the pictures.
Read the words.
Write them in your ESL notebook.

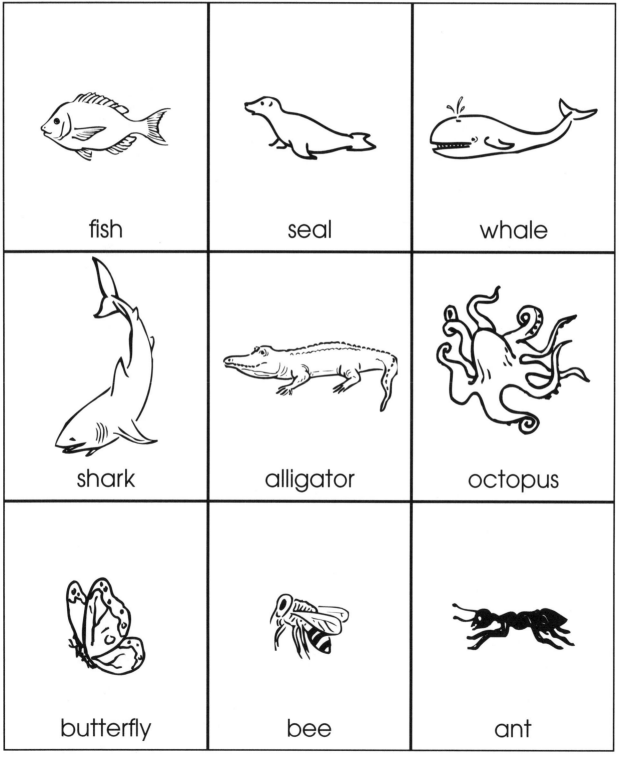

fish	seal	whale
shark	alligator	octopus
butterfly	bee	ant

See instructions on pages T14–T15.

Draw a Brown Cow

Draw each animal.
Copy the animal name on the line.
Color each picture.

1. brown **cow**	2. gray **mouse**
COW	
3. yellow **bee**	4. black **horse**
5. orange **monkey**	6. purple **hippopotamus**

K-2 Newcomer Program • Prentice Hall Regents © by Judie Haynes

See instructions on page T20.

Draw a Green Turtle

Draw each animal.
Copy the animal name on the line.
Color each picture.

1. green **turtle**	2. blue **fish**
turtle	
3. gray **whale**	4. brown **bear**
5. yellow **lion**	6. green **alligator**

See instructions on page T20.

K-2 Newcomer Program • Prentice Hall Regents © by Judie Haynes

What Animal Is This?

Connect the dots. Start with *a*.

a b c d e f g h i j k l m
n o p q r s t u v w x y z

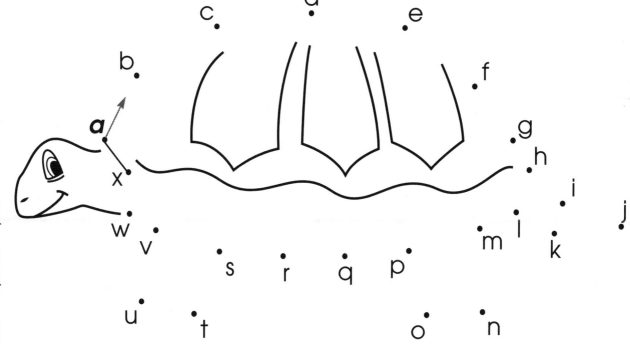

This is a _____.

K-2 Newcomer Program • Prentice Hall Regents   © by Judie Haynes

See instructions on page T20.

Name _____   Date _____

Jungle or Ocean?

Color the pictures. Cut them out.
Glue each picture in the correct place.

Jungle	Ocean

monkey

whale

tiger

octopus

seal

shark

snake

parrot

See instructions on page T25.

K-2 Newcomer Program • Prentice Hall Regents   © by Judie Haynes

Where Do They Live?

Color  *(green)* **animals
that live in a tree.
Color** *(brown)* **animals
that live on the ground.**

deer	squirrel	bear
parrot	duck	rabbit
owl	turtle	monkey

See instructions on page T27.

What's in the Egg?—1

Color the pictures.
Cut them out.
Put them in the correct order.

K-2 Newcomer Program • Prentice Hall Regents © by Judie Haynes

What's in the Egg?—2

Glue the pictures from page 168 in the correct order.

1	2
3	4
5	6

See instructions on page T18.

Name _____ Date _____

Animal Word Search

Find each word in the puzzle.
Circle it.

elephant	mouse	owl	bat	tiger
octopus	whale	deer	cow	parrot
monkey	zebra	duck	fish	cat
hippopotamus	turtle	sheep	rabbit	dog
kangaroo	lion			

```
O K O X Y D O G R H C E C M X
Y C B W C O H M A I M Z W W U
E S T J L M F O B P O C X H R
R L H O O W D N B P U Z C A T
G N E E P H U K I O S O O L T
N I C P E U C E T P E Q B E U
C F R A H P S Y J O A R M V R
K I D A T A B D D T Z B H Y T
Z S E T F J N C E A E G P B L
I H X K L F B T E M B P P R E
X L C W C Z E P R U R A T X B
V K A N G A R O O S A R J J A
L L I O N X V T I G E R P L T
X K T O U O U E C O W O G A B
S L O U P E D U C K J T Y L H
```

See instructions on page T19.

K-2 Newcomer Program • Prentice Hall Regents   © by Judie Haynes

Animal Crossword

Look at the clues.
Fill in the puzzle with animal words.

Across

Down

K-2 Newcomer Program • Prentice Hall Regents   © by Judie Haynes

See instructions on page T25.

Draw the Animals—1

Read page 173.
Draw the animals in this picture.

K–2 Newcomer Program • Prentice Hall Regents   © by Judie Haynes

Draw the Animals—2

A. Draw the animals in the picture on page 172.

1. Draw a fish in the water. Color it orange.

2. Draw a turtle on the log. Color it green.

3. Draw a snake in front of the log. Color it brown.

4. Draw a bird on the branch of the tree. Color it blue.

5. Draw a duck next to the rock. Color it yellow.

6. Draw a rabbit behind the tree. Color it white.

7. Draw a bee over the grass. Color it yellow.

8. Draw a deer between the trees. Color it brown.

B. Write a sentence about four of the animals. Example: The fish is in the water.

1. _____

2. _____

3. _____

4. _____

See instructions on page T27.